# EDUCATION
# FOR
# CREATIVITY

## TRAINING, RESEARCH, AND IMPLICATIONS

# EDUCATION
# FOR
# CREATIVITY

## TRAINING, RESEARCH, AND IMPLICATIONS

By

Dr. Pramod K. Gupta

M. Phil., Ph.D.

Cosmo Publications

2004 New Delhi

**CREATIVITY FOR EDUCATION**


First Published by COSMO 2004

ISBN 81-7755-867-6

**Published by**
MRS. RANI KAPOOR
for COSMO PUBLICATIONS
Publishing Division of
GENESIS PUBLISHING PVT. LTD.
24-B, Ansari Road, Darya Ganj,
New Delhi-110 002, INDIA

**Composed at**
Cosmo Publications

**Printed at**
Mehra Offset Press

# Contents

# PREFACE

From the stone age to the present age, man has always been in search of superior off-springs because he knew that only the best would survive in the competitive world of tomorrow. It has been true for any society. In fact, it is the superiority of human creativity which has ultimately made the difference in the progress of various societies. Developing countries are not able to make satisfactory progress not because they don't have the natural resources but because they are unable to tap the precious creative potential of their human resources. Therefore, nothing can contribute more to the progress of a society than fostering the creative performance of its people. Education is perhaps the best instrument to help in this regard.

The need, therefore, is that the educational system of a society must encourage creativity in its pupils, if the society wants to develop along new directions. From this point of view, the research on creativity and its development has become an extremely relevant area of educational inquiry in recent years. During the past forty years, studies are being conducted to explore the various aspect of creativity. The question whether creativity can be developed or not has attracted the exclusive attention of researchers in last twenty-five years. The present book titled "Education

For Creativity" focuses its attention on this very issue and tries to answer some of the basic questions with regard to the development of creativity, *viz.*, Is creativity developable? Can creativity be taught or trained? How can creativity be developed? Can creativity be developed by providing deliberate education and training in creativity?

While answering these questions, the book has discussed in depth the rational to support the view that creativity can be developed through appropriate education and training. Further, the book emphasizes that the creativity is not just the by-product of our educational system rather a special kind of training is required for its development. In one chapter, the description of that creativity training programme has been given in detail which may be of much interest for the readers. The work is vastly different in its approach from other works published in India. It is hoped that the book may come out as the most informative and valuable reference material in one cover for researchers in the area of creativity development.

Though the book presents the result of a research work, it is primarily intended to benefit all those who are interested to know more about creativity. It will be specially useful for teacher, educators and researchers who would like to know how can the creative potential of school children be developed? Further, it may be interesting for the parents and general readers who would like to have a basic understanding about the concept of creativity and its development. Besides, many educational administrators, managers may find this book useful, if they wish to nurture creativity in their institution.

In the end, I would like to express my gratitude to all those who encouraged me in completing this work. At first place, I owe my deep sense of gratitude to Dr. J. P. Srivastava, Department of Education, Institute of Advanced Studies, Meerut University, Meerut for his valuable guidance and suggestions at every step of the present work. Without his direction, this work would have never materialized. I just don't have words to convey my thanks to Dr. R. S. Pandy, Prof. & Head, Deptt. of Education, University of Allahabad for his sincere encouragement and blessings at a time when its was most needed. In fact, he has been a source of continuous inspiration for me throughout this work. I must acknowledge my sincere thanks to Prof. Renjulli, University of Connecticut (USA) for sending the related literature at the initial stage of the study.

Through It cannot be claimed that this is the only exclusive work in the field but it would be a great satisfaction for me if the book could serve even a small fraction of society.

Deptt. of Education, (Pramod K. Gupta)
North Eastern Hill University,
Nagaland Campus, Kohima.

# one

## CONCEPTUAL FRAMEWORK: EDUCATION OF CREATIVITY

### The Context: Need for Training Creativity

There has always been a concern in all nations of the world to develop a system of education which could produce original thinkers to help the society develop along new directions. But no one would dispute the fact that so far this endeavour has failed in our country. The system of education in India is facing grave crises these days. At one hand, it is becoming non-productive and non-creative, on the other hand, it is facing numerous problems like wastage and stagnation, mass illiteracy and brain drain resulting in a great loss of creative potential every year. This disappointing performance of the schools has led many educational thinkers of the present day world to demand the establishment of "de-schooled society" and to explore alternatives to schools.

In order to develop the society, it has been considered necessary to provide knowledge and skills in the schools. The importance of knowledge can not be denied, but knowledge alone is not enough. The remarks of Baquer Mehdi (1975)[1] are worth mentioning here that "if education today is to give something to its future citizen, it is not knowledge or information which is imparted in the class rooms, nor the certificates or the degrees which they receive at the end of their schooling as a passport for their future employment, but a creative mind which would enable them to adjust and readjust themselves in the fast changing world in which they live today".

It is true that we can not turn each child into a creative person, but it is also true that each child during the period of his growth and development can be trained to think in a creative manner so that in one field or another he may be able to make use of his ability and have the satisfaction of having realized his creative talents at least to some extent. The review of research literature (Tylor, 1959[2]; Parnes and Brunelle, 1967[3]; Torrance and Torrance, 1973[4]; Mansfield, Busse and Krepelka, 1978[5]; Passi and Jarial, 1983[6] Rose and Lin, 1984[7]) show that children when trained to think creativity do a much better job in terms of production of new ideas than those who are not given this kind of training. It has also been shown (Ebel *et al.*, 1969)[8] that like other abilities creative thinking abilities too get stultified when not properly cared for and stimulated.

In education we have a powerful instrument to enable man to rise to higher and still higher levels of intellectual efficiency. We can give our education a new meaning and a new orientation if the emphasis is shifted from a mere routine type of learning to creative thinking. Not only will the transfer value of such a training be enormous but it will also enable us to tap more effectively our vast reservoir of creative talent that is lying dormant in almost every individual and which due to lack of proper stimulation is largely wasted (Mehdi, 1975)[9].

Thus, we find that education is to shoulder a great responsibility to determine to what extent creativeness and creative production can be improved in school children and how shall this be done. It is in this context, these seems to be a need to make an effort for answering the question whether or not creativity in school children can be improved by providing training in creative thinking through some specific instructional material in the Indian context.

**Importance of Creativity and its Development**

Creativity has become a rapidly expanding area of scientific enquiry since it has been considered a subject of study of almost unparalleled significance for human welfare (Raina, 1980)[10]. Never before has there been so strong a demand for the search of creativity as there is today. Whether it is considered from the view points of its effects on society, or as one of the expressions of the human spirit, creativity stands out as an activity to be studied, cherished and cultivated (Arieti, 1976)[11]. In one form or the other, there is a world-wide concern about creativity. Advanced countries are definitely interested in this study and the development of creativity, as are the developing countries whose survival depends upon the creative vision and creative striving of the masses.

The business world took interest in creativity because it was felt that the increase in the number of novel things and maximum possible profit are dependents on new ideas. The psychologists studying human personality were inclined to study creativity as it had become clear that the balanced development of human personality is not possible without adequate actualization of creative potential. Now, it is admitted every where that a creative individual succeeds very easily in his personal as well as vocational life. Among educators, there are very legitimate reasons why should they be so much concerned about the development of creativity in school children. In this context, some of the reasons needed discussion which will clarify the importance of creativity and its development.

*Global Perspective*

No doubt, the scientific and technological advancement has added remarkably to our civilization and comforts but it is also true that it has created numerous problems for the mankind which had never existed earlier. The world of today is passing a crucial phase of its history. The threat of an atomic war capable of destroying the planet, unlimited population growth, serious ecological risks and energy crises are forcing mankind to think of some new alternatives for survival (Gupta, 1984)[12]. As we foresee the future, there seems to be a constant threat to the world peace. It is ironic that we can spend billions of dollars to send man to the moon and back and yet allow more pressing problems here on earth to go relatively unattended.

Behind all our progress and the problems created out of that, there have been people who had the 'wonderful gift of creativity' in abudnance. It is this creativity which has now put us into trouble and the same can save us from the future dangers also. The world's energy resources may be limited but the possibilities of the human brain is certainly not. Like any other ability brain is also gifted with the ability to think creatively which is never ending.

The unprecedented progress of science and advancement of technology have further given a set back to man's position. The present computer dominated age seems more and more to reject man as a performer of routine tasks and a solver of routine problems. Computer now can perform a great number of tasks and solve many problems with much greater efficiency than can man. Such a technological cultural, if it is to continue its growth, demands less of man's physical energy and more of his creative ideational process.

And finally, it needs hardly be mentioned that at no times in the history of human civilization have there been changes in the life of man so vast and so rapid as they are now and it can be taken for granted that the pace of change is bound to be still faster in the years to come. In this flux not only does knowledge which the invidicual has acquired at a considerable cost gets obsolete too soon but also our children who acquire this knowledge through the same cycle of memorising and passing examinations year after year are rendered incapable of using their minds productively and creatively.

In these complex situations of modern society, our future as a nation is unquestionably bound by the availability of creative mind in an increasingly large number. The new challenges of our time can be met only by the people who have been trained to use their minds creatively. What education, therefore, should aim at in the present context of our life is to infuse creative thinking among our pupils. The school is the only place where perhaps an organized effort can be made to ensure a continuous flow of such creative mind.

*Social Significance*

It has generally been agreed by all societies that their survival and progress will eventually depend upon how effectively they can conserve and utilize their most precious human resources—their creative children. All development in every shaper of activity in the nation springs from the way the creative potential of its children is fostered and encouraged. In this connection Barron (1968)[13] has rightly remarked that "Our capacity for creative thought and action may literally make all the differences in the world".

The history of development and achievement in the world are the instances of the fact that it were the creative persons who changed the course of history by their discoveries and inventions. In fact historical records provide evidence that cultures have collapsed because of the failure to utilize the intelligent and imaginative methods for solving their problems.

At this point Arnold Toynbee's (1962)[14] pertinent observation seems to be correct that: "To give a fair chance to potential creativity is a matter of life and death for any society. This is all important, because the outstanding creative ability of fairly small percentage of the population is mankind's ultimate asset and the only one with which man has been endowed...If society fails to make the most of his human asset or if, worse still, it perversely sets itself stifle it. Man is throwing away his birth right of being the lord of creation and is condemning himself to be instead; the least effective species on the face of this planet".

Seen in this light, development of creative potential assume crucial importance in the progress of any society. This is more true in the case of developing countries like ours. Hence the earlier we spot out and nurture the creative potential of our children, the better it would be. Torrance (1962)[15] is of the view that "the future of our civilization-our very survival-depends upon the quality of the creative imagination of our next generation". This remark clearly warns that the development of creativity should be a definite aim of education and not left as a by-product of social condition, if society is to maintain and facilitate its growth and progress.

The schools happens to be an important agency of education and it is obligatory on the part of society to know whether the creative potential of its children are being looked after properly or not. Thus, it becomes imperative for a nation to chalk out adequate programme to provide the children opportunities for the actualization of their creative potential. This is essential for the mere survival of a nation.

*Individual Necessity*

Development of creativity and concern for it is not only a social reality but an individual necessity also. We say that education in a democracy should help individuals to develop their talents fully. This has long been a widely approved purpose of education. Schools are anxious that the children they educate grow into fully functioning persons. But, in recent times, there have been pressures to limit this to intellectual talents only. Even with this limited definition of the goals of education, the abilities involved in creative thinking can not be ignored. Certainly, we can not say that one is fully functioning mentally, if the abilities involved in creative thinking remain undeveloped. These are the abilities involved in becoming aware of problems, thinking up possible solutions and testing them. If their functioning is impaired, one's capacity for coping with life's problems is indeed marginal (Torrance, 1962)[16].

Furthermore, there is also little doubt that one's creativity is his most valuable resource in coping with life's daily stresses. It is this release of creative potential which provides release to the blocked mental energy and thus leads a man for a sound mental health. It is a step towards the self-actualization and self-satisfaction. The blockage of creative potential may lead to mental tension and confusion in children. The similar opinion is expressed by Patrick (1955)[17] when he says: "the stifling of creativity cuts at the very roots of satisfaction and ultimately creates overwhelming tension and breakdown". The above remark clearly indicates that creativity is a necessary resource in one's life to develop himself into fully functioning mentally healthy person. This is one of the legitimate concern of education to help their students in avoiding mental breakdown and achieve healthy personality growth by providing enough opportunities for the release of creative potential through various school programmes (Torrance, 1962)[18].

*Academic Value*

Almost no one would deny the legitimacy of the school's concern with educational achievement of children. It is time and again contended that schools are meant for maximising the student's learning and academic achievement. To achieve this objective, it has been the notion among school workers that intellectual abilities like cognition, memory and convergent thinking should be given high priority as against divergent or creative thinking. Thus, they appear to favour authorative teaching or learning by authority whereby giving more emphasis on memorization. They believe that this sort of teaching is more effective and economical. It further gets support when students get high marks in examination.

But, the academic achievement which students receive from the existing educational system after being examined at the end of year can not be considered valid for their performance on the ground that the examinations which often succeed in making correct prediction about academic achievement, test only those intellectual abilities of children which involve cognition, memory and convergent thinking, the sole indicator of our so believed I.Q. as measured by the traditional intelligent tests. It has now been realized that traditional measures of intelligence succeed in assessing only a few of mental abilities which are supposed to be responsible for academic success.

It is pointed out by Raina (1975)[19] that about 90 per cent of our student population can be above average and so gifted in the variety of talents. But confining to so known academic success, it has been found that only about 10 per cent of our student population are above average. It means that our present educational system with its stereotype curriculum and teaching methodologies cater to the needs of these 10 per cent of students population only without any care of rest of the 90 per cent students.

At present, school curriculum does not provide an opportunity for the students to explore their creative potential. Recent and on-going studies (Torrance, 1962)[20], show that even traditional subject matter can be taught in such a way that the creative thinking abilities are important for their acquisition. It will help in both academic achievement and as well as creative performance. The very fact that some high I.Q. do poorly in school and some lower I.Q. students do well indicate that intelligence, as conventionally assessed, is not the only quality making for educational success. Intelligence exerts an effect on achievement upto a threshold level beyond which increment in I.Q. do not make any difference but divergent thinking does (Ebel, 1969)[21]. Seen in this light the treatment of creativity is an important as any other ability from educational point of view.

In conclusion, it can be observed that any system of education in a society should encourage creativity so that a society can be saved from stagnation and the individual can also have his own fulfilment. Thus, we find that creativity is entering into the curriculum of a school as well as in its evaluation. Studies are being made about the nature of creativity, how it grows, how it can be nurtured, how it can be measured and predicted and so on. But, the question whether creativity can be developed or not is still open.

**Neglect of Creative Potential**

Home, Society and School play a vital role in developing creative thinking in children. The best environment for creative children is the home but parents, while wishing to foster creativity, go about it, the wrong way. They are more concerned with external success and popularity instead of with inner growth and creative potential of their children. They show anxiety if their children do not conform to their wishes. In a society where economic success and competition is important, most parents brain wash their children into believing that every thing must be sacrified in order to be successful. Thus, they hinder the flow of creative potential of their children.

Society too have been cruel in developing creative thinking in children. Our society is so orthodox that we are not ready for any change. Any new thinking is curbed before it is expressed. Many people strongly believe that whatever exists today, is final and unchangeable. The vested interests in the society always oppose any type of contemplated change. We have always been making fun of those people who are different from ordinary people.

It has been found that sometimes a person has to keep away from his social relations because of his unconventional behaviour (which is due to his creative thinking) and also that a number of creative people prefer to be a ordinary one in order to establish pleasant social relations (Dutt and Lal; 1977)[22].

Not only this, we feel satisfied and proud of what we had in our ancient period. We have been consoling ourselves with the glory of our past that we had even atom bombs and the reference to such weapons can be traced to the holy scriptors. Doing so at one hand we postpone our further original thinking and pay homage to the western technology most unconsciously on the other hand. This is what Huxley calls "Cultural Shock". A society lives creatively if it maintains adequate equilibrium on the rope and continues to move forward. Unfortunately, this is not happening in our present day society and as a result of this creative potential of its people is not flourishing (Dutt and Lal, 1977)[23].

After home and society, school is supposed to be an effective instrument for accelerating creative growth of young children. It is the bounden duty of schools to ensure that it produces creative children who make a useful contribution for the advancement of society and for the attainment of national goals. But the kind of education that we have been providing does not result in this.

There is some reason to believe that the large number of schools hinder the development of creativity instead of facilitating it. When the child comes to school, he is full of eagerness, curiosity and sensitivity. His capacity for wonder knows no limits. He strives to know each and every thing about the world in which he lives. But once in the school, he has to change himself in accordance with the commands of his teachers and expectations of his peers. Excessive spoonfeeding snatches all initiative from them. Consequently, the poor children fail to recognize their creative potential.

One of the most justifiable charge that can be labelled against our educational system is that it has neglected and all too often suppressed, the natural creativity of the young (Kneller, 1965)[24]. Education in our society is almost systematized and routinized at all levels from primary to the university. It has encouraged and has been encouraging listless passivity and rote memory. It is generally seen that our school programmes are not giving due place to the educational experience and proper environment which are conducive to the development of creative potential. This tragedy is beyond description.

Do our schools in any way encourage the creative potential to flourish? Do we attach any importance to creativity in our school programme today? The whole educational system and the expectations of parents and teachers who themselves are the successful products of the conventional system of education and social structure, kill the very spark of creativity in children. Our system of examination, curriculum, method of teaching, instructional strategies and text books are not in consonance with the development of this ultimate human asset.

Ebel (1969)[25] quotes Bloom and maintains that: "There is reason to believe that educational system can reduce originality and creativity. This negative effect on creativity is most marked when examinations, instructional materials and processes, all emphasize learning by rote and the goal is centred on getting through examination". This is exactly what is happening in most of our schools today-creativeness is being stifled and ordinariness promoted. The whole school curriculum is geared to success rather than the achievement for its own sake. All this leads to what researchers call the "other directed personality" with emphasis on immediate action and short term goals.

Thus, we find that our present educational system neglects systematic search and promotion of creativity in our students and thus much creative talent goes unrecognized. In this connection, Kothari Commission[26] (1964) has rightly reported, "Even the talent that enters school and succeeds in climbing the educational ladder does not flower fully because it is not discovered sufficiently early and is studying in poor school. For obtaining the best results in quality, talent has to be located early and allowed to grow in the best atmosphere and under the best teachers".

There is, therefore, a need to re-examine, remodal or drastically change, if necessary, our existing school programmes, if we want to achieve our educational goals. The pendulum must swing from anti-creative education to creative education which encourages many kinds of talents and many degree of excellence.

**The Present Problem**

Although, the research has consistently shown that all children have the potential to think creatively and that creative production can be improved by providing children with learning experiences that encourage them to use their creative thinking (Torrance, 1965[27]; Williams, 1968[28]; Edwards, 1968[29]). Many secondary school teachers experience a great deal of difficulty when they attempt to encourage children to express themselves creatively. Part of this difficulty is due to their inability in creating a conducive environment for the stimulation of creativity, but the problem is also a result of their failure to teach students for the basic skills of creative thinking.

A considerable amount of research has been done in recent years to determine ways and means of developing creativity among school children. On the question whether creativity can, in fact, be developed, research workers are generally agreed that education can do a great deal in this direction. Research studies (Torrance, 1972)[30] have indicated that creativity can be developed by deliberate procedures.

In this connection, an issue of prime importance is whether or not it is possible to train people to think more creatively? In other words, is it possible to develop some kind of instructional programme which may help children to make more effective use of their imagination, find more original solutions to the problems they face daily and discover new ways of looking at old problems? Concern for this issue has resulted in the present study which has been titled as follows:

> "Development and Evaluation of Creativity Training Programme for VI Grade Children".

Thus, the purpose of this study is to develop a systematic creativity training programme (CTP) and to report the results of the experiment conducted to determine its effectiveness alongwith the reactions of children towards CTP.

## Objectivies of the Study

The following objectives have been set up for the present study:

(1) To develop a creativity training programme (CTP) for VI grade children.

(2) To study the effect of creativity training programme (CTP) upon the development of fluency component of verbal creativity (Verbal fluency) in VI grade children.

(2a) To study the interaction effect of CTP and level of intelligence on the development of fluency component of verbal creativity (verbal fluency) in VI grade children.

(2b) To study the interaction effect of CTP and sex on the development of fluency component of verbal creativity (verbal fluency) in VI grade children.

(2c) To study the interaction effect of level of intelligence and sex with CTP on the development of fluency component of verbal creativity (verbal fluency) in VI grade children.

(3) To study the effect of creativity training programme (CTP) upon the development of flexibility component of verbal creativity (verbal flexibility) in VI grade children.

(3a) To study the interaction effect of CTP and level of intelligence on the development of flexibility component of verbal creativity (verbal flexibility) in VI grade children.

(3b) To study the interaction effect of CTP and sex of the development of flexibility component of verbal creativity (verbal flexibility) in VI grade children.

(3c) To study the interaction effect of level of intelligence and sex with CTP on the development of flexibility component of verbal creativity (verbal flexibility) in VI grade children.

(4) To study the effect of creativity training programme (CTP) upon the development of originality component of verbal creativity (verbal originality) in VI grade children.

(4a) To study the interaction effect of CTP and level of intelligence on the development of originality component of verbal creativity (verbal originality) in VI grade children.

(4b) To study the interaction effect of CTP and sex on the development of originality component of verbal creativity (verbal originality) in VI grade children.

(4c) To study the interaction effect of level of intelligence and sex with CTP on the development of originality component of verbal creativity (verbal originality) in VI grade children.

(5) To study the effect of creativity training programme (CTP) upon the development composite

verbal creativity in VI grade children.

(5a) To study the interaction effect of CTP and level of intelligence on the development of composite verbal creativity in VI grade children.

(5b) To study the interaction effect of CTP and sex on the development of composite verbal creativity in VI grade children.

(5c) To study the interaction effect of level of intelligence and sex with CTP on the development of composite verbal creativity in VI grade children.

(6) To study the effect of creativity training programme (CTP) upon the development of originality component of non-verbal creativity (non-verbal originality) in VI grade children.

(6a) To study the interaction effect of CTP and level of intelligence on the development of originality component of non-verbal creativity (non-verbal originality) in VI grade children.

(6b) To study the interaction effect of CTP and sex on the development of originality component of non-verbal creativity (non-verbal originality) in VI grade children.

(6c) To study the interaction effect of level of intelligence and sex with CTP on the development of originality component of non-verbal creativity (non-verbal originality) in VI grade children.

(7) To study the effect of creativity training programme (CTP) upon the development of elaboration component of non-verbal creativity (non-verbal elaboration) in VI grade children.

(7a) To study the interaction effect of CTP and level of intelligence on the development of elaboration component of non-verbal creativity (non-verbal elaboration) in VI grade children.

(7b) To study the interaction effect of CTP and sex on the development of elaboration component of non-verbal creativity (non-verbal elaboration) in VI grade children.

(7c) To study the interaction effect of level of intelligence and sex with CTP on the development of elaboration component of non-verbal creativity (non-verbal elaboration) in VI grade children.

(8) To study the effect of creativity training programme (CTP) upon the development of composite non-verbal creativity in VI grade children.

(8a) To study the interaction effect of CTP and level of intelligence on the development of composite non-verbal creativity in VI grade children.

(8b) To study the interaction effect of CTP and sex on the development of composite non-verbal creativity in VI grade children.

(8c) To study the interaction effect of level of intelligence and sex with CTP on the development of composite non-verbal creativity in VI grade children.

(9) To find out the reactions of the students towards the creativity training programme.

**Rationale of the Study**

The present study is based on the rationale that the creative performance of an individual is dependent on to what extent his creative potential is developed. Though, the degree of creative performance is determined by the degree of creative potential inherited by an individual, but it can not be expected from a child that he would be able to manifest his creative potential in his creative performance up to a optimum level unless he is provided enough opportunities to develop it. Not only this, even the tests would fail to assess his actual creative potential in this case, if it is measured before it has been given chance to develop (Murty, 1972)[31]. Thus, the development of creative potential seems to be of much importance than the mere possession of it.

Before any further consideration on the development of creativity, it would be relevant to review some of the questions and problems fundamental to creativity.

(i) How does creativity grow at various age and grade levels?

(ii) What is the role of intelligence in the development of creativity?

(iii) What is the role of environment in the development of creativity?

(iv) Is creativity developable?

(v) Can creativity be taught or trained?

(vi) How can creativity be developed?

The overview of the related literature in the field of creativity provides needed theoretical foundations to get the answer of the above questions and problems which, in turn, explains the rationale of the present study.

***Developmental Patterns of Creativity (How does Creativity Grow at Various age and Grade Levels):***

Like any other mental ability, creativity also has its characteristic developmental trends which have been studied extensively. Torrance (1962)[32], reviewing a number of earlier studies on the growth of creativity and giving results from many studies conducted by himself at Minnesotta, has described at length the developmental trends for creative abilities. The following are some general conclusions drawn on the basis of these studies:

*(a) Age wise Development:* A child begins to develop his imagination during the first two years of his life. He also shows signs of curiosity but how he expresses it, depends upon his unique characteristics. From age two to age four, the child develops a sense

of autonomy, indulges in verbal and imaginative play, makes new discoveries for himself and explores his capacities and abilities. A typical child from four to six years has good imagination though it has also been observed that during these years, there is also a lessening of imagination. After this, up to eight years of age, the child becomes aware of other's feelings and his realistic imagination develops.

From eight to twelve years, the child develops his imagination still further and can use his skills creatively in many areas. The faculty of critical reading gradually develops and a general restlessness is felt by the child. After twelve years of age, the spirit of adventure reigns in social and emotional fields. During this period, seeds of non-conformity against adult rules and regulations are also shown. This is continued till fourteen years of age after which, most of the imaginative activity seems to be focused on the future career. The skills involved in creative problem solving are slowly learnt during this period though adventure still occupies an important part in life. However, peer acceptance and unstable nature of interests and aptitudes may dampen the creativity of sixteen years old boys and girls. A sixteen to eighteen years old youth is full of optimistic aspirations for his life and considers arts and social activity as means of enriched living. He develops the ability to channelize his emotional energy creatively and to solve problems of complex nature.

After the age of eighteen years, it is rather difficult to speak of common development patterns of creative abilities with age because of the great diversity in vocations chosen by individuals. Nevertheless, it is more or less established that productions of the highest quality tend to fall off at an earlier age (in the thirties) and decline slowly afterwards. In some individuals, the decline is very slow even in old age, whereas others "burn" themselves out rather quickly due to various reasons.

*(b) Grade wise development:* On the basis of the framework provided by Torrance (1962)[33], it can be said that there is a steady growth of creative abilities from grade one through grade three. From thereon, there is a slump between the third and the fourth grade which is followed by a little recovery during grade five and six. Another slump occurs between the sixth and the seventh grade after which, there is again an almost steady growth until near the end of high school years. At grade eleven, there is however, again some set back. It has also been observed that even though recovery takes place during grades five and six yet the third grade status is not again exceeded until grade nine (for boys) and grade ten (for girls).

Many explanations have been given to explain the set backs in the growth of creative abilities at the fourth, seventh and eleventh grade levels respectively. According to Torrance (1962)[34] these declines may be explained in terms of "...... reactions to new stresses encountered at each new stage of development or each transitional state in education".

The developmental trends with respect to creativity as discussed above shows that the children develop their creative potential more rapidly at the age of 10-12 years and/or around grade six. It is due to this reason that the investigator decided to conduct the study on VI grade students who by and large fall in the age group of 10-12 years.

*Intelligence and Creativity (What is the role of Intelligence in the development of creativity?)*

For a long time, it was believed that the persons who are creative are endowed with a high degree of intelligence. But, the recent researches have disproved this assumption and on contrary it has been persistently demonstrated that the intelligence and creativity have only a low positive correlation (Ebel *et al.*, 1969)[35]. This is of course on the assumption that there is a cut-off score of I.Q. around the normality above which aforesaid relationship holds good (Deshmukh, 1977)[36].

After presenting a through review of literature Torrance (1967)[37] summarizes the correlational information about creativity and intelligence relationship as revealed in various studies. He found that from the total of 178 coeffecticients of correlation between the measures of intelligence and total measures of creativity, the median was 0.20; thus, indicating the relationship between creativity and intelligence as low. It shows that it is not necessary for a highly creative person to have high intelligence. The person with low intelligence may almost as likely to be creative as the one with high intelligence. On the other hand, a highly intelligent person may not necessarily be highly creative. To explain this, what can we say is that an intelligent but not creative person may be capable of sustained abstract thought, but he may not be unable to produce more original ideas. Conversely, a person who is creative but not too intelligent is unable fully to develop his insights because he lacks the capacity for prolonged abstract thinking (Kneller, 1965)[38].

The general conclusion with respect to intelligence and creativity is that a certain degree of intelligence is required, if one is to be creative, but beyond that point intelligence and creativity become independent of each other. It has been estimated that an I.Q. of at least 120 is generally necessary for high creativity, the level varying according to the nature of creative activity (Kneller, 1965)[39]. Scientists may require high level of intelligence than paintes and musicians.

Thus we see that the level of intelligence has not to do much with creative performance. Dutt (1975)[40] is of the opinion that intelligence is a stepping stone towards creativity, just as memory is a stepping stone towards intelligence. What is more important than the level of intelligence is the effectiveness with which a person uses it for his creative performance. In the light of above discussion, it can safely he assumed that children of all intelligence level are capable of being creative.

Keeping the above facts in mind, it was decided to have intelligence as one of the variable in the study so that its effect on the development of creativity (through CTP) can be studied.

*Environment and Creativity (What is the role of environment in the development of creativity?)*

With regard to the development of creativity, there is a common belief that the child will become creative of his own accord, if only he can be placed in a stimulating environment. No doubt, an environment which is stimulating plays an important role in establishing the conditions necessary for creative output but this is only part of the story. Environment, however, can not supply what the person lacks. In order to take full advantage of an un-restrictive atmosphere, the child first must come to understand what constitute creative ideas in the given situation and low can he achieve such ideas for himself. In short, he must learn how to think creatively (Convington, 1968).[41]

Thus, it appears that the child must have at his disposal a repertoire of creative thinking skills in order to think creatively (Covington, 1968)[42]. Though it can not be ignored that the creative thinking can be promoted by providing stimulating environment, but on the basis of above mentioned facts it is felt that the direct training in the basic skills of creative thinking would be more effective in developing creativity among children.

*Developability of Creadivity (Can Creativity be developed?)*

Regarding the development of creative ability, there are two different views. One believes that all mental abilities are heriditory and can not be developed (Calton, 1969)[43] while according to the other mental abilities are skills which can be developed through appropriate education and training. (Guilford, 1962[44]; Parnes and Prunelle, 1967[45]; Torrance, 1972[46]; Rose and Lin, 1984[47]).

Torrance (1967)[48] is of the opinion that heridity does not place limits upon creative development and achievement. Creative abilities are inherited to the extent that a person inherits his sense organs, peripheral nervous system, and brain. How these abilities develop and function, however, is strongly influenced by the way the environment responds to a person's curiosity and creative needs.

Thus, it seems that the environmental influences are more important in the development of creativity.

Even if we assume that creative thinking abilities are hereditary, the expression of creative potential will depend upon the environmental influences including education and training. It means that if the degree of creative expression can be increased by environmental manipulation, it can be said that creativity is capable of being developed.

Therefore, it is the application aspect of an ability that is more important than the mere possession of it. This calls for the teachers to educate his pupils in such a way that its manifestation reaches its perfection. In conclusion, we can say that creativity is developable provided it gets chance to develop.

*Trainability of Creativity (Can creativity be taught?)*

It is now well known fact that the development of creativity is being neglected in our schools. Therefore, the challenge before us is to stop stifling creative thinking and on the other hand train the children to think creatively. But, the question is - can we train creative thinking.

Guilford (1963)[49] is of the opinion that creativity involves some specific kind of thinking abilities and each of which may be looked upon as a distinct kind of thinking skill. If we know, what kind of skill it is we can help it to develop by providing training with the help of appropriate curriculum material. Just as teachers are trained by developing their teaching skills, children can also be trained to think creatively by developing their creative thinking skills.

Olton and Crutchfield (1968)[50] also agrees that appropriate training can produce significant increments in the skills of creative thinking, since the development of any kind of skills (Motor or Mental) requires specific training. The same views have been expressed by Mehdi (1975)[51] and Deshmukh (1977)[52].

Further, there are sufficient evidences to the fact that creativity can be taught or trained (Guilford, 1972[53]; Oltan and Crutchfield, 1968[54]; Torrance, 1972[55]; Parnes, 1976[56]). If it is so, the creative thinking skills needed for creative behaviour, can be identified and then some ways can be explored to establish these skills in the student's repertoire with the help of appropriate instructional material.

In the light of the above discussion, it seems that creative thinking can be taught or trained through some systematically designed instructional programme which could bring about a substantial increase in the extent to which a student utilizes his potential for creative thinking (Olton, 1968[57]; Covington, 1968[58]; Rose and Lin, 1984[59]).

*Approaches to Develop Creative Thinking (How can Creativity be Developed?)*

Psychologists and educationists have tried number of ways to develop creativity. An analysis of research studies reveals that there may be the following three broad approaches to develop creative thinking among school children in class room situation:

(i) Providing creative climate.

(ii) Using creative teaching methods.

(iii) Training creativity directly.

*(i) Providing Creative Climate:* It has been shown (Parnes, 1967)[60] that creativity can be developed by providing a climate which is conducive to creativity. In creative climate, children are given freedom to express their ideas without any fear. Their unusual questions and imaginative ideas are respected by the teacher. They are asked open ended questions which stimulate their thinking instead of asking conventional types of questions having one right answer. Deshmukh (1977)[61] has listed four types of activities, namely, searching, organizing, originating and communication for creating a conducive environment for the development of creativity. Torrance (1961)[62] has emphasized reward as a crucial factor in maintaining creative atmosphere. He has given five principles for rewarding creative thinking.

(a) Treat unusual questions with respect.

(b) Treat unusual ideas with respect.

(c) Show children that their ideas have value.

(d) Provide opportunities for self-initiated learning and give credit for it.

(e) Provide periods of non-evaluated practice.

Renzuli (1972)[63] agrees with Torrance and maintains that the atmosphere conducive to creativity can be established only when the children are rewarded for their creative behaviour.

Research (Parnes, 1967)[64] also appears to show that an environment which asks for creative behaviour and rewards it, helps to close the gap between an individual's creative potentiality and his creative productivity. In such a climate, individuals with high potential for creativity are more likely to be recognized and encouraged to actualize the potential.

*(ii) Using Creative Teaching Methods:* Besides establishing the atmosphere conductive to creativity various teaching methods are also employed to develop creative thinking in children. This approach may be termed as creative teaching.

By creative teaching we mean teaching a concept, relation or skill through a technique that involves the student's creative thinking abilities (Gorman, 1968)[65].

In such type of teaching, the teacher teaches the subject matter in a way that encourages student's original thinking. Children are asked provocative questions regularly that call for their divergent thinking *e.g.*, what would happen if .....? To promote pupil's creativity, they are encouraged to manipulate ideas and objects in different ways, to toy around with various combinations of ideas, to list the parts of an object and then think of different ways to change each part, and similar activities.

Hallman (1967)[66] while commenting on creative teaching says—"Research literature supports the position that creativity indeed can be taught, but that it can not be taught by the traditional and authoritarian methods. Creative procedures can not be prescribed nor can they be written into lesson plans; yet creative teaching is the best way, perhaps the only way to promote creative behaviour on the part of pupils".

Torrance (1967)[67] has emphasized that the teachers must develop certain creative teaching skills, if they want to develop creative talent in students. He has given a list of some important teaching skills as given below:

(a) Recognizing and acknowledging the potentialities of the students.
(b) Being respectful of questions and ideas.
(c) Asking provocative questions.
(d) Recognizing and valuing originality.
(e) Developing creative reader.
(f) Applying scientific approach in solving a problem.
(g) Using unevaluated practice and experimentation.
(h) Guiding planned experiences.

Different techniques have been adopted in creative teaching. Parnes (1967)[68] has listed number of techniques such as attribute listing (Crawford, 1954), brain storming (Osborn, 1953), morphological analysis (Zwicky, 1957), synectics (Gordan, 1961), Role playing (Moreno, 1947; Torrance, 1975), check list (Davis, 1969), Such man's inquiry training technique (1962, 1966), Luthe's creativity mobilization technique (1976), Osgood's general somentic (1957), Garadin's Bionies (1968), forced relationship, word association and many others.

*(iii) Training Creativity Directly* Recently, attempts have been made to train pupils' creativity directly. Here, instead of using creative teaching methods, children are directly taught, how to think creatively? In this approach, children are given instruction on the nature of creative process and creative thinking abilities. They are given practice and training in creative thinking skills.

This is the most direct approach in teaching creativity. It also take use of different techniques as already discussed in creative teaching. A brief retrospect of advances and developments in training for creativity during last thirty years is given below:

(a) *Work books and ideas books*

Osborn (1953)[69] and Parnes (1967)[70] have developed text books and work books for the students of their creative problem solving programmes. A guide book (Parnes, 1967) for teachers with 300 problems and topics has also been prepared. These, the work book and guide book, have been very recently revised and published as "Creative Action Book and the Guide to Creative Action" (Parnes, Noller and Binodi, 1966)[71].

Myers and Torrance have prepared a series of idea books which include experiences for developing intellectual skills involved in creative thinking, *viz*:—

(i) Invitation to thinking and doing (1964)[72].

(ii) Can you imagine (1965a)[73].

(iii) Invitation to speaking and writing creatively (1965b)[74].

(iv) For those who wonder (1966a)[75].

(v) Plots, Puzzles and Plays (1966b)[76].

Exercises in these idea books are creative and are based on the research findings of the basic research undertaken by the authors and other research workers in the field.

(b) *Audio-Visuals*

Besides the work books, ideas books, and guide books, there is a large variety of audio-visuals aids available for use in creativity training. Cunningham, Myers and Torrance (1965)[77] have developed 'Imagi/Craft' material to develop creative thinking in elementary school children. It consists of recorded planned sequences of creative thinking activities, *viz.*, "Great Moments of Discovery", "Great Moment in Invention", "Great Moment in Geographical Discovery", and "Fantasies".

These materials involve dramatized recordings of highlights of some discoverers such as Alexender Grahm Bell. It attempts to familiarize children with nature and value of creative achievement, the problems of the creative persons and creative ways of thinking and finding out things. It involves the children in the kind of thinking similar to those displayed by the great discoverer. The teacher's guides are also available.

"Sound and Images" is another audio-visual material developed by Cunningham and Torrance (1965)[78] to stimulate created thinking. It is a recorded device for obtaining images in response to four different sounds of varying complexity and strangeness with some exercises. Students are asked to respond to the sound effects and name them. Exercises are repeated three times with the instruction of free thinking.

Other programme using audio-tapes are "The Golden Key to the Problem Solving", "Releasing the Energy of Ideas" etc. These are actually slide talks, comprising a set of coloured slides with accompanying tapescript. They are produced by creative education foundation and are being used in their regular creative problem solving courses.

Recently Luthe (1976)[79] has developed Creativity Mobilization Technique (CMT) which uses crayon and brush as media for developing creativity through paintings. Another interesting experiment was conducted at California Institute of Technology. They used a computer to find out which brain processes result in creative thought and explored that by the rapid stimulation of brain functions on machine, a nearly infinite number of hypotheses about human thinking can be tested.

(b) *Packaged Programmes*

In recent years, a large variety of packaged programmes have been developed to train creative thinking in school children. These programmes contains exercises similar to measures of creativity. They are based on the assumption that creative thinking abilities can be strengthened by giving students exercises similar to the tests measuring the particular abilities (Guilford, 1962)[80].

Covington *et al.* (1965)[81] prepared "The Productive Thinking Programme" which attempts to develop auto-instructional material for creative development. The programme was further revised in 1974[82]. It consists of 15 creative problem activities in the form of detective mysteries designed primarily for the V and VI grade children. Activities are presented in a self-instructional linear format. A story line is maintained throughout the series of lessons to give the reader a set of identification models. It gradually introduces him to the process of becoming a more effective thinker by teaching him to define the problem in his own words, to plan to attack it, to check ideas against pertinent facts, to search for many and unusual ideas, to look at the problem from different points of view and to avoid jumping to conlcusions.

Feldhusen *et al.* (1971)[83] designed Purdue Creative Thinking Programme for the children at IV grade level. It consists of 28 audio-tapes, each accompanies by a printed exercise providing practice in divergent thinking skills. Each audio-tape consists of a three to four minutes presentation with specific creative thinking suggestions, followed by a ten-minute historical story featuring an American Pioneer.

Frank William (1970[84], 1972[85]) has also developed a very comprehensive programme based on his CAI model for individualizing and humanizing the learning process. This programme package consists of instructor's manual; five volumes written on different aspects of creative reaching *viz.*, "identifying and measuring creative potential"? "teachers work book", "media resource book", class room ideas for encouraging thinking and feeling; two poster sets *viz.*, "thinking feeling process and teaching strategies"; two tape cassettes *i.e.*, "teacher training audio tape cassettes"; and demonstration lessons audio tape cassettes; and a "teaching strategies packet," which completes the programme.

Parnes (1967)[86] too has developed, administered

and evaluated a set of 28 booklets on the five phases of creative procees *viz.*, orientation, observation, manipulation, and evaluation. These booklets are part of a creativity course of 26 sessions. In this course students are taught the principles of creative thinking and then asked to practice them on problem exercises as well as on their own problems. These booklets are so designed that each student can stretch his imagination for full forthy minutes on each one. This material can be used effectively with or without instructor.

Renjulli *et al.* (1973)[87] developed a creativity training programme entitled "New Directions in Creativity" which is in five volumes *viz.*, Mark 1, 2, 3, A and B. Each volume of the programme contains 24 types of creativity training activities and a teacher's guide that includes suggestions for individualized instruction and follow-up programming. Two activity sheets, each containing one or more exercises are provided for each type of activity.

The foregoing discussion on the training for creativity lead to the conclusion that these three approaches can be used to develop creative thinking in children. But, as discussed earlier, environmental approach alone can not help in stimulating creativity because environment can not supply what the person lacks. In order to take full advantage of an creative atmosphere, the child must learn 'how to think creatively'. Creative teaching approach requires creative teachers who are difficult to find and moreover no serious of fort is made to teach teachers for developing creative talent in children.

Thus, direct training for creativity seems to be the right approach in the present circumstances as it can be used without bothering to change the present curricular and administrative set up, without demanding modification of teacher class room variables and without any material aid that will involve financial implications.

**Assumptions Facts about Creativity**

Many of the assumptions about creativity which underlie current discussion and research differ from those previously held. In this connection, Gilchrist (1972)[88] observation is pertinent to quote that "the application of the word creativity to ordinary school children is a departure from identifying creativity with the great man or genius and reflects the belief that creative talent is distributed through out the population and is present to some degree in every child. Concern with educational practices and fostering creativity assumes that creative talent may be encouraged or hindered by environmental influences and departs from earlier beliefs (such as those of Galton) which emphasized the hereditary basis of ability and attached little importance to experiences in the learning situations provided by home and school".

One of the bright sports in creativity research (as opposed to research on intelligence a generation ago) is that we go into it not with the feeling that creativity is fixed and unchangeable (as the I.Q. was once thought to be), but we consider creativity as responsive to environmental stimulation, and therefore, dependent upon our educational efforts (Gowan, 1965)[89].

In the light of above view the present study is based on the following assumptions:

(i) Abilities involved in being creative are universal. In other words, every body can be creative to some extent in one way or the other. Here the observation of Murphy (1947)[90] seems to be correct that:

> "the desire to create must be almost universal and that almost everyone has some measure of originality which stems from his fresh perception of life and experience, and from the uniqueness of his own fantasy when he is free to share it".

This view is further supported by Louis Fliegler (1961)[91] when he says that:

> "All individuals are creative in diverse ways and to different degrees. The nature of creativity remains the same whether one is producing a new game or symphony ...... Creativity is within the realm of each individual depending upon the area of expression and capability of the individual".

(ii) If it is reasonable to suppose that to some

extent all men are creative, it is also reasonable to assume that some of the variation in creativity results from the failure of many to express their creative potential (Kneller, 1965)[92]. It has been found that children of all ability level demonstrate a level of thinking that fall far short of what they are potentially capable for creative thought (Covington, 1968)[93]. It may be due to the fact that creative potential of our children is not being tapped properly in our class rooms.

(iii) Psychologists and Educationists are of the opinion that creative behaviour is a learned behaviour. If it is so, it can be developed. This view is supported by Parnes (1976)[94] when he says:

> "Like most behaviour, creative activity probably represents to some extent many learned skills. There may be limitations set on these skills by heredity, but I am convinced that through learning one can extend the skills within those limitations."

Thus, creativity, though can not be created, but it can certainly be cultivated. In other words, creativity which is latent is capable of being developed.

(iv) If creativity is capable of being developed, it can be taught also. Just as teachers are trained by developing their teaching skills, children can also be trained to think creatively by developing their creative thinking skills through appropriate education and training.

Olton and Crutchfield (1968)[95] are of the opinion that appropriate training can produce significant increments in the skills of creative thinking, since the development of any kind of skills (motor or mental) requires specific training.

Research has also shown that children can be taught to make fuller and appropriate use of their capacities by means of a systematic and direct training (Covington, 1968)[96].

(v) If it is true that creativity can be taught, the appropriate instructional material can also be designed which could bring about a substantial increase in the extent to which a student utilizes his potential for creative thinking (Olton, 1968).[97]

In the light of the above assumptions, it can safely be concluded that there exists a pronounced gap between creative potential and creative performance and that this gap can be narrowed by deliberate education in creative thinking.

## Hypotheses

Keeping in mind the objectives of the present study and rationale involved as discussed earlier, the investigator formulated the following null hypotheses:

$^{H}1$. There is no significant difference in the mean gain scores of the verbal fluency between the students of the treatment groups who are given training through CTP and the students of the non-treatment group who did not get such training.

$^{H}1.1.$ There is no significant interaction of the level of intelligence with CTP on the development of verbal fluency.

$^{H}1.2.$ There is no significant interaction of sex with CTP on the development of verbal fluency.

$^{H}1.3.$ There is no significant interaction of the level of intelligence and sex (combined) with CTP on the development of verbal fluency.

$^{H}2$ There is no significant difference in the mean gain scores of the verbal flexibility between the students of the treatment group who are given training through CTP and the students of non-treatment group who did not get such training.

$^{H}2.1.$ There is no significant interaction of the level of intelligence with CTP on the development of verbal flexibility.

$^{H}2.2.$ There is no significant interaction of sex with CTP on the development of verbal flexibility.

$^{H}2.3.$ There is no significant interaction of the level of intelligence and sex (combined) with CTP on the development of verbal flexibility.

$^{H}3.$ There is no significant difference in the mean gain scores of the verbal originality between the students of the treatment group who are given training through CTP and the students of the non-treatment group who did not get such training.

$^{H}3.1$. There is no significant interaction of the level of intelligence with CTP on the development of verbal originality.

$^{H}3.2$. There is no significant interaction of sex with CTP on the development of verbal originality.

$^{H}3.3$. There is no significant interaction of the level of intelligence and sex (combined) with CTP on the development of verbal originality.

$^{H}4$. There is no significant difference in the mean gain scores of the composite verbal creativity between the students of the treatment group who are given training through CTP and the students of non-treatment group who did not get such training.

$^{H}4.1$. There is no significant interaction of the level of intelligence with CTP on the development on composite verbal creativity.

$^{H}4.2$. There is no significant interaction of sex with CTP on the development of composite verbal creativity.

$^{H}4.3$. There is no significant interaction of the level of intelligence and sex (combined) with CTP on the development of composite verbal creativity.

$^{H}5$. There is no significant difference in the mean

gain scores of the non-verbal originality between the students of treatment group who are given training through CTP and the students of the non-treatment group who did not get such training.

$^{H}5.1$. There is no significant interaction of the level of intelligence with CTP on the development of non-verbal originality.

$^{H}5.2$. There is no significant interaction of sex with CTP on the development of non-verbal originality.

$^{H}5.3$. There is no significant interaction of the level of intelligence and sex (combined) on the development of non-verbal originality.

$^{H}6$. There is no significant difference in the mean gain scores of the non-verbal elaboration between the students of the treatment group who are given training through CTP and the students of non-treatment group who did not get such training.

$^{H}6.1$. There is no significant interaction of the level of intelligence with CTP on the development of non-verbal elaboration.

$^{H}6.2$. There is no significant interaction of sex with CTP on the development of non-verbal elaboration.

$^{H}6.3$. There is no significant interaction of the level of intelligence and sex (combined) with CTP on the development of non-verbal elaboration.

H7. There is no significant difference in the mean gain scores of the composite non-verbal creativity between the students of the treatment group who are given training through CTP and the students in the non-treatment group who did not get such training.

H 7.1. There is no significant interaction of the level of intelligence with CTP on the development of composite non-verbal creativity.

H 7.2. There is no significant interaction of sex with CTP on the development of composite non-verbal creativity.

H7.3. There is no significant interaction of the intelligence and sex (combined) with CTP on the development of composite non-verbal creativity.

## Definitions of the Terms Used

The present study involves some important terms which need to be defined operationally so that the further discussion may be understood in the proper context.

(i) *Creativity*

A survey of related literature reveals that different thinkers view creativity differently. But, there is almost a consensus among thinkers that creativity is an ability to break away from the usual sequence of thought into an altogether different pattern of thought as a result of which some thing new is brought to the existence which is novel and previously unknown to the producer.

For the purpose of the present study, the term creativity is operationally defined "as a group of mental abilities underlying the divergent thinking operation of intellect which involves chiefly the abilities of fluency, flexibility, originality and elaboration, the measurement of which is possible with the help of creativity tests, both verbal and non-verbal".

The above definition further involves the following key terms:

(a) Divergent thinking.
(b) Fluency.
(c) Flexibility.
(d) Originality.
(e) Elaboration.

These terms are defined as given below:

(a) *Divergent thinking:* It is a process in which a person thinks in different directions in order to produce something new. When the divergent thinking process acts upon the somentic content, it results into verbal creativity and when it acts upon the figural content, it results into non-verbal creativity.

(b) *Fluency:* It is the ability to think of number of solutions of a problem. Thus, it refers to the quantity of output in a given time.

(c) *Flexibility:* It is the ability to think through different approaches. Thus, it refers to the variety of output.

(d) *Originality:* It is the ability to think up unusual solutions. Thus, it referes to the quality of output.

(e) *Elaboration:* It is the ability to think up complete details of an idea. Thus, it refers to the comprehensiveness of output.

### (ii) *Development of Creativity*

It refers to the increase in creative performance which may be due to the natural growth or training through education. Thus, the development of creativity can be observed in the gain of creative performance during a particular period of time.

### (iii) *Creativity Training Programme (CTP)*

It refers to a set of instructional material that contains within it systematically organized learning activities for developing creative thinking skills in children.

### (iv) *Evaluation*

It refers to the attempt to study the effect of creativity training programme on the development of various components of creativity. This effect has been analysed in terms of the increase in creative performance which has been obtained by testing creative thinking level of the students before and after they undergo training through CTP.

**Delimitations of the Study**

The present study is delimited to its following areas as under:

*Population:* The study is limited to the population of VI grade children studying in Hindi medium schools of Haldwani town of Nainital district in U.P. Only those schools were considered in the population which are run by the government. Thus, the public schools run by the private bodies do not fall in the target population. Further, co-educational schools were also not considered.

*Sample:* The study is limited to the sample of 357 student of class VI selected from two schools (*viz.*, one boys and one girls school) of Haldwani town of Nainital district in U.P.

*Creativity Training Programme:* The development of creativity training programme is limited to the area of verbal and non-verbal creativity only.

*Evaluation:* In the present study, the evaluation is confined to the determination of the effectiveness of the creativity training programme upon the development of the various components of verbal and non-verbal creativity in children.

**Foot Notes:**

1. Baquer Mehdi. The Background Paper. In Baquer Mehdi (Ed.) *Creativity in Teaching and Learning.* Report of the workshop conducted at the Regional College of Education, Mysore from 27th Jan. to 1st Feb., 1975, RCE, Mysore, NCERT, New Delhi, 1975, pp. 1-4.
2. C.W. Taylor. *Research Conference on the Identification of Creative Scientific Talent.* Salt Lake City, University of Utah, 1959.
3. S.J. Parnes and E.A. Erunelle. The Literature of Creativity (Part I). *Journal of Creative Behaviour,* Winter 1967, Vol. 1, No. 1, pp. 52-109.
4. E.P. Torrance and J.P. Torrance. Is Creativity Teachable? Bloomington, Ind: *Phi Delta, Kappa,* Educational Foundation, 1973.
5. R.S. Mansfield, T.V. Busse and E.J. Krepelka. The Effectiveness of Creativity Training. *Review of Educational Research.* Fall 1978, Vol. 48, No. 4, pp. 517-536.
6. B.K. Passi and G.S. Jarial. Researches in Creativity Training in India: A Review. In Govind Tewari and Roma Pal (Editors), *Status of Indian Researches in Creativity,* Agra Psychological Research Cell, Agra, 1983, pp. 45-54.
7. L.H. Rose and Hsin-Tai Lin. A meta analysis of Long Term Creativity Training Programmes. *Journal of Creative Behaviour,* 1984, Vol. 18, No. 1, pp. 11-22.
8. R.L. Ebel, M.B. Rogers and H.N. Victor (Ed.) *Encyclopaedia of Educational Research,* IV Edition, Collier, Macmillan, London, 1969.
9. Baquer Mehdi. The Background paper. In Baquer Mehdi (Ed.) *Creativity in Teaching and Learning.* Report of the workship conducted at the Regional College of Education, Mysore from 27 th????? 1975 RCE Mysore ECERT.

10. M.K. Raina. *Creativity Research: International Perspective,* NCERT, New Delhi, 1980.

11. S. Arieti. *Creativity: The Magic Synthesis,* New York, Basic Books, 1976.

12. P.K. Gupta. Education for Creativity: A Global Issue *NEHU Journal of Social Science and Humanities,* North-Eastern Hill University, Shillong, Vol. II, No. 1, Jan-March, 1984, pp. 27-30.

13. F. Barron. *Creativity and Personal Freedom,* New Jersey, D. Van Nostrand Company, Inc., Princeton, 1968.

14. Toynbee, Arnold, (1951). Is America neglecting her Creative Minority? In C.W. Taylor (Ed.) *Widening Horizens in Creativity,* New York. John Wiley and Sons, Inc., 1964.

15. E.P. Torrance, *Guiding Creative Talent,* Prentice Hall, 1962, pp. 1-15.

16. E.P. Torrance. *Guiding Creative Talent,* Prentice Hall, 1962, pp. 1-15.

17. C. Patrick, *What is Creative Thinking?* Philosophical Library Inc., New York, 1955.

18. E.P. Torrance. Causes for Concern. In P.E. Vernon (Ed.) *Creativity.* Penguin Books Limited, England, 1970, pp. 355-370.

19. M.K. Raina Multi-talent Teaching Approach. Baquer Mehdi (Ed.) *Creativity in Teaching and Learning.* Report of the workshop conducted at the Regional College of Education, Mysore from 27th Jan. to 1st Feb., 1975, RCE, Mysore, NCERT, New Delhi, 1975, pp. 16-19.

20. E.P. Torrance. *Guiding Creative Talent.* Prentice Hall, 1962, pp. 1-15.

21. R.L. Ebel, M.B. Rober and H.N. Victor, *Encyclopaedia of Educational Research,* Fourth Edition, The Macmillan Company, London, 1969.

22. N.K. Dutt and g. Lal. *The Creative Potential and Education,* Indian Book Agency, Ambala Cantt, 1977, pp. 34-39.
23. N.K. Dutt and G. Lal. *Creative Potential and Education.* Indian Book Agency, Ambala Cantt, 1977, p. 45.
24. G.F. Kneller. *The Art and Science of Creativity.* New York: Holt, Rinehart and Winston, 1965.
25. R.L. Ebel, M.B. Rogers, H.N. Victor. *Encyclopaedia of Educational Research.* IV Edition, Collier-Macmillan, London, 1969.
26. Kothari Commission Report, Ministery of Education, Govt. of India, New Delhi, 1964-66.
27. E.P. Torrance. *Rewarding Creative Behaviour: Experiments in Class room Creativity.* Englewood Cliffs, NJ, Prentice Hall, 1965.
28. Frank E. Williams. *Media for developing creative Thinking in Young children.* Buffalo, New York, Creative Education Foundation, 1968.
29. M.O. Edwards. A Survey of Problem Solving Course. *Journal of Creative Behaviour,* 1968, Vol. 2, pp. 33-51.
30. E.P. Torrance. Can we Teach Children to think Creatively? *Journal of Creative Behaviour.* 1972, Vol. 6, pp. 114-143.
31. Vasudev, Murty. Report of the Proceedings of a Siminar held at Department of Physics, Aligarh Muslim University, Aligarh from 10 to 12 Feb., 1972. In Baquer Mehdi (Ed.) *Creativity and Undergraduate Science Education,* Aligarh Muslim University, Aligarh.
32. E.P. Torrance. *Guiding Creative Talent.* Englewood, N.J. Prentice Hall, 1962, pp. 84-103.
33. E.P. Torrance. *Guiding Creative Talent.* Englewood, N.J. Prentice Hall, 1962, pp. 84-103.
34. E.P. Torrance. *Guiding Creative Talent.* Englewood, N.J. Prentice Hall, 1962, pp. 84-103.

35. R.L. Ebel; M.B. Roger; H.N. Victor. *Encyclopaedia of Educational Research.* Fourth Edition. The Macmillan Company, Collier-Macmillan Ltd., London, 1969.
36. M.N. Deshmukh. Teachability of Creativity. *Journal of Indian Education.* July, 1977, Vol. III, No. 2, pp. 45-50.
37. E.P. Torrance. The Minknesotta studies of Creative Behaviour: National and Interanational Extensions. *Journal of Creative Behaviour,* 1967, Vol. 1, pp. 137-154.
38. G.F. Kneller. *The Art and Science of Creativity.* Holt, Rinehart, Winston, 1965, p. 10.
39. G.F. Kneller. Ibid, 1965, p. 10.
40. N.K. Dutt. *Psychological Foundations of Education.* Doaba House, Delhi-6, 1975, p. 219.
41. M.V. Covington, Promoting Creative Thinking. *Journal of Experimental Education,* 1968, Vol. 37, No.1, pp. 22-30.
42. Ibid, pp. 22-30.
43. F. Galton. *Heriditory Genius,* Macmillan, London, and Appleton, 1869.
44. J.P. Guilford (1963). Can Creativity be increased by Practice? In Gowan, J.C., Domos, G.D., and Torrance, E.P., (Editors). *Creativity: Its Educational Emplications,* New York. John Wiley and Sons, 1967, pp. 150-157.
45. S.J. Parnes and E.A. Brunelle. The Literature of Creativity (Part I). *Journal of Creative Behaviour,* 1967, Vol. I, pp. 52-109.
46. E.P. Torrance. Can we Teach Children to Think Creatively? *Journal of Creative Behavior,* 1972, Vol. 6, No. 2, pp. 114-143.
47. Laura Hall. Rose and Hsin-Tai. Lin. A Meta-analysis of Long Term Creativity Training Programmes. *Journal of Creative Behaviour,* 1984, Vol. 18, No.1, pp. 11-12
48. E.P. Torrance. Nurture of Creative Talents. In G.A. Davis

and J.A. Scott, (Editors). *Training Creative Thinking*, Holt, Rinehart and Winston, Inc., New York, 1970, p. 208.

49. J.P. Guilford. Can creativity be increased by practice? In J.C. Gowan, G.D. Domas, and E.P. Torrance (Editors). *Creativity: Its Educational Implications.* New York, John Wiley and Sons, 1967, pp. 150-151.
50. R.M. Olton and R.S. Crutchfield (1968). Developing the Skills of Creative Thinking. In Davis, G.A. and Scott, J.A. (Editors). *Training Creative Thinking*, New York, Holt, 1971, pp. 237-260.
51. Baquer, Mehdi (Ed.). Creativity in Teaching and Learning. Report of the workshop conducted at Regional College of Education, Mysore from 27th Jan to 1st Feb., 1975, RCE, NCERT, New Delhi, p. 3.
52. M.N. Deshmukh. Teachability of Creativity. *Journal of Indian Education*, July, 1977, Vol. 3, No.2, pp. 45-50.
53. J.P. Guilford (1963). Frontiers in Thinking that Teachers should know about. In Gowan, J.C.; Domas, G.D.; and Torrance, E.P. (Editors). *Creativity: Its Educational Implications*, New York, John Wiley and Sons, 1967, pp. 150-157.
54. R.M. Olton and R.S. Crutchfield (1968). Developing the Skills of Creative Thinking. In G.A. Davis; and J.A. Scott. (Editors). *Training Creative Thinking*, New York, Holt, 1977, pp. 237-260.
55. E.P. Torrance. Can we Teach Children to think Creatively? *Journal of Creative Behaviour*, 1972, Vol. 6, pp. 114-143.
56. S.J. Parnes, (1967). Education and Creativity. In Gowan, J.C.; Domas, G.D.; and Torrance, E.P.; *Creativity: Its Educational Implications*, New York, John Wiley and Sons, 1967, p. 33.
57. R.M. Oltan. A Self Instructional Programme for Developing

Productive thinking Skills in V and VI grade children. *Journal of Creative Behaviour,* 3(1), 1968, p. 16.
58. M.V. Covington. Promoting Creative Thinking. *Journal of Experimental Education,* 37(1), 1968, pp. 22-30.
59. Laura Hall, Rose and Hsin-Tai, Lin. A Meta-analysis of Long Term Creativity Training Programmes. *Journal of Creative Behaviour,* 18(1), 1984, 11-22.
60. S.J. Parnes (1967). The Literature of Creativity (Part II). *Journal of Creative Behaviour,* 1967. Vol. 2, pp. 191-239.
61. M.N. Deshmukh (1977). Teachability of Creativity. *Journal of Indian Education.* NCERT, New Delhi, July, 1977, Vol. III, No. 2, p. 47.
62. E.P. Torrance (1961). Giving children a chance to Learn and Think Creatively. In E.P. Torrance, *Education and Creative Potential.* The University of Minnesotta Press, Minneapolis, 1963, pp. 56-58.
63. J.S. Renjuli. *New Directions in Creativity,* Harper and Row, New York, 1973, p. 10.
64. S.J. Parnes. The Literature of Creativity (Part II), *Journal of Creative Behaviour,* 1967, Vol. 2, pp. 191-239.
65. R.M. Gorman, *The Psychology of Class room Learning - An Inductive Approach.* Charles E. Merrill Pub. Company, Columbus, Chio, 1968.
66. R.J. Hallman. Techniques of Creative Teaching. *Journal of Creative Behaviour.* Creative Education Foundation, 1967, Vol. 1, pp. 325-330.
67. E.P. Torrance (1967). Nature of Creative Talents. In Davis, A.G. and Scott, J.A.; *Training Creative Thinking.* Hall, Rinehart and Winston, Inc., New York, 1971, pp. 208-219.
68. S.J. Parnes. Methods and Educational Programmes for Stimulating Creativity: A Representative list. *Journal of Creative Behaviour.* Vol. 2, No. 1, 1967.

69. A.F. Osborn. *Applied Imagination,* New York, Charles Scribner's Sons, 1953, (Indian Edition), St. Paul Publications, Allahabad, 1971.
70. S.J. Parnes. *Creative Behaviour Work book,* New York, Charles Scribner's Sons, Inc., 1967.
71. S.J. Parnes, R.B. Noller, and A.M. Binodi, *Guide to Creative Action.* Revised Edition of Creative Behaviour Guide Book. New York: Scribner, 1977.
72. R.E. Myers and E.P. Torrance. *Invitation to thinking and doing.* Boston, 1964.
73. R.E. Myers and E.P. Torrance, *Can you Imagine.* Boston, 1965(a).
74. R.E. Myers and E.P. Torrance. *Invitation to speaking and writing Creatively,* Boston, 1965(b).
75. R.E. Myers and E.P. Torrance. *For those who wonder,* Boston, 1966 (a).
76. R.E. Myers and E.P. Torrance. *Plots, Puzzles and Plays,* Boston, 1966 (b).
77. B.F. Cunningham, R.E. Myers and E.P. Torrance, *Imagi/Craft.* Massachusetts, Lexington, Ginn and Company, 1965.
78. B.F. Cunningham; and E.P. Torrance. *Sounds and Images,* Boston: Ginn and Company, 1965.
79. W. Luthe. *Creativity Mobilization Technique.* New York: Crune and Stratton Inc., 1976.
80. J.P. Guilford. Creativity: Its Measurement and Development. In S.J. Parnes and H.F. Harding (Eds.). *A Source Book for Creative Thinking,* New York. Scribner, 1962, pp. 151-158.
81. M.V. Covington, R.S. Crutchfield, and L.B. Davis. *The Productive Thinking Programme.* Berkeley: Brazelton Printing Co., 1965.
82. M.V. Covington, R.S. Crutchfield, L.B. Davis, and R.M. Olton. *The Productive Thinking Programme - A Course in Learning to Think:* Columbus, Chio, Merrill, 1974.

83. J.E. Feldhusen, S.M. Speedie, and D.J. Treffinger. The Purdue Creative Thinking Programme. Res. and Evaluation. *National Society for Performance and Instruction Journal.* 1971, Vol. 10, No. 3, pp. 5-9.

84. F.E. Williams. *Class room Ideas for Encouraging Thinking and Feeling.* Buffalo: D.O.K. Pub., 1970.

85. F.E. Williams. *A Total Creativity Programme for Individualizing and Humanizing the Learning Process.* Englewood Cliffs, New Jersey: Educational Technology Publications, 1972.

86. S.J. Parnes. Methods and Educational Programmes for Stimulating Creativity: A Representative list. *Journal of Creative Behaviour,* 1967, Vol. 2, No. 1.

87. J.S. Renjulli. *New Directions in Creativity.* New York, Harper and Row, 1973.

88. M. Gilchrist. *The Psychology of Creativity.* Melbourne University Press, Carlton, Victoria, 1972, p. 8.

89. J.C. Gowan (1965). What makes a gifted child creative? Four Theories. In J.C. Gowan; G.D. Damos and E.P. Torrance (Eds.) *Creativity - Is Educational Implications.* John Wiley, New York, 1967, p. 15.

90. G. Murphy. *Personality,* New York, Harper and Row, 1947, p. 453.

91. L. Fliegler. Dimensions of Creative Process. In Michael Andrews (Ed.), *Creativity and Psychological Health,* Syracuse, N.Y.; Syracuse University Press, 1961, p. 14.

92. G.F. Kneller. *The Art and Science of Creativity.* Holt, 1965, p. 14.

93. M.V. Covington. Promoting Creative Thinking. *Journal of Experimental Education,* 1968, Vol. 37, No. 1, pp. 22-30.

94. S.J. Parnes (1976). Education and Creativity. In Gowan, J.C.; Demos, G.D.; and Torrance, E.P.; *Creativity: Its Educational Implications.* John Wiley and Sons, New York, 1967,

p. 33.

95. R.M. Olton; and R.S. Crutchfield (1968). Developing the skill of creative thinking. In Davis, G.A.; and Scott, J.A.; (Eds.) *Training Creative Thinking,* New York, Holt, 1971, pp. 237-260.
96. M.V. Covington. Promoting Creative Thinking. *Journal* of Experimental Education, 1968, Vol. 37, No. 1, pp. 22-30.
97. R.M. Oltan. A Self Instructional Programme for developing Productive Thinking Skills in V and VI grade Children. *Journal of Creative Behaviour,* 1968, Vol. 3, No. 1, p. 16.

# two

## THE RESEARCH REVIEW

Finding of the earlier research work provide an empirical frame work for the conduct of further research study. It is in this reference that the researches so far conducted in the area of the development of creativity consitute a significant base for the present study. Keeping this in view, it is essential to have a stock of existing research literature in the field. For this purpose, the review of earlier research studies is of utmost importance. This chapter is devoted to this task.

### A Preview of the Research Efforts

Though, the study of creativity in a scientific fashion is a quite recent phenonenon, but a large number of studies dealing with the various aspects of creative thinking have appeared in various publications of psychological and educational importance in current years. The credit of this large expansion of research goes to J.P. Guilford[1] who called the attention of the researchers while giving his presidential address to the American Psychological Association in 1950 about the dearth of research literature in the field of creativity. It has been estimated that the number of studies for the eighteen months of 1965 and 1966 equated with that of the preceding five years, which in turn equalled that of the preceding ten years, which in its turn equalled that of the preceding 100 years (Parnes and Brunelle, 1967)[2]. After that, a huge amount of research literature have been produced during last 17 years between 1967 and 1984. In all these studies, researchers have attempted to answer the following four types of question with regard to the creativity:

1. What is the nature of creativity?
2. How can creativity be measured?
3. How creativity is related with other variables?
4. Can creativity be developed? If yes, how?

The question, whether creativity can be developed or not has attracted the exclusive attention of researchers in the recent years. The review of research literature during last 25 years or so, reveals that a considerable amount of research has been done to determine ways and means of developing creativity among school children. Though the researchers have tried various methods and procedures to develops creativity in children, but it seems that only a few attempts have been made to design a systematic creativity training programme which make use of instructional material for this purpose. Moreover, their findings are also not conclusive on account of some methodological limitations.

A further review of the related literature would bring to light the various procedures and methodologies which have been employed to develop creativity among children and which ones have remained unexplored. This would explain the importance and necessity of the present study.

As various methods have been employed by different researchers for developing creativity, the research literature to be reviewed is classified into the following different captions according to the procedure followed by them:

1. Creative thinking technique.
2. Transcedental meditation.
3. Teaching methods.
4. Instructional material.
5. Other procedures.

It is to be noted here that only those studies are the subject of the present review which are directly concerned to the development of creativity. Further, the studies conducted abroad and in India are reviewed separately following the same captions as mentioned above except the last one which was not required with regard to the Indian studies.

## Research Scenario: Abroad

During last two and half decade, a large number of studies dealing with the developmental aspect of creativity have been conducted in abroad. The review of these studies have been done from time to time and the reviewers have indicated the possibility of development of creativity. Before the further literature in the field is reviewed, it would be worth to have the preview of some earlier reviews.

Parnes and Brunelle (1967)[3] while reviewing the literature on creativity have identified two types of educational efforts to facilitate creative functioning and development:

(i) Deliberate training programmes designed to remove internal blocks.

(ii) Provision for environmental conditions that eliminate external blocks to such performance.

This review included over forty studies evaluating programmes for teaching students to improve their sensitivity, fluency, originality, elaboration and related abilities. These investigations range from the retarded level to the gifted level and from the first grade through college and adult education. Studies of adults have involved subjects from such diverse groups as military officers, teachers and industrial personnel. Approximately ninety per cent of the total number indicate that subject's creative productivity levels were significantly increased by deleberate educational programmes.

Torrance and Torrance (1973)[4] conducted a comprehensive survey of various research studies to answer the question "Is Creativity Teachable?" The survey included 142 research studies which provide information about the trainability of creativity. The studies are classified into nine categories according to the method employed. The summary of the analysis is given below:

| S. No. | Procedure followed | No. of studies | No. of success | Percentage of success |
|---|---|---|---|---|
| 1. | Creative problem solving procedures (like Osborn and Parnes methods) | 22 | 20.00 | 91 |
| 2. | Other disciplined approaches | 5 | 4.60 | 92 |
| 3. | Complex programmes involving packages of materials (such as Purdue Creativity Training Programme, Covington *et al*'s productive thinking programme and Torrance Idea Books etc.) | 25 | 18.00 | 72 |
| 4. | Creative arts as vehcle | 18 | 14.50 | 81 |
| 5. | Media & Reading Programmes | 10 | 7.80 | 78 |
| 6. | Curricular and administrative arrangements (designed to create favourable conditions for promoting creative thinking) | 8 | 4.00 | 50 |
| 7. | Teacher Variables, Class room climate etc. | 26 | 14.40 | 55 |
| 8. | Motivation, Reward and competitions etc. | 12 | 8.00 | 67 |
| 9. | Facilitating Testing Conditions | 16 | 11.00 | 69 |
| | Total | 142 | 102.30 | 72 |

The percentage of success of these nine types of procedures in developing creativity ranged from 50 per cent (curricular and administrative arrangements) to 92 per cent (other disciplined approaches). The most favourable approaches seem to have been through complex programme involving packages of materials (such as Purdue Creativity Training Programme, Covington's Productive Thinking Programme etc.) with 72 per cent success and manipulating teacher variables and class room climate with 55 per cent. The later approach can not be relied upon much as its percentage of success is quite low as compared to the former one.

Mansfield, Busse and Krepelka (1978)[5] surveyed sixty five studies, designed to develop creative thinking abilities of the subjects through a few specially designed programmes for creativity development, namely, the productive thinking programme (Covington, Crutchfield, Davies, and Olton, 1966), the Purdue Creative Thinking Programme (Feldhusen, Speedie and Treffinger, 1971), the Parnes Programme (Sidney Parnes, 1967), the Myers-Torrance Work Books (Myers and Torrance, 1964, 1965, 1966, 1968), the Khatena's Training Method (Khatena, 1970, 1971, 1973), and a few other training programmes (Shackel and Lawrence, 1969; Franklin and Richards, 1977; Goor and Rappoport, 1977; Dellas, 1971; True, 1966; Meicheubaum, 1975; and Korth, 1973). The review showed that inspite of a few methodological limitations, most of the studies have shown the effectiveness of these training programmes in enhancing the creativity scores of the subjects.

Very recently, Rose and Lin (1984)[6] have compiled the data from a wide range of research studies on creativity training and analyzed the effectiveness of various training programmes by applying a new statistical technique of meta-analysis developed by Glass (1978)[7].

For this analysis, researchers included 46 studies which were divided into six groups as follows according to the types of training programme or treatment:

1. Osborn-Parne's Creative Problem Solving Programme (CPS) and its modification: 8 studies.
2. Covington's Productive Thinking Programme (PTP): 5 studies.
3. Prudue Creative Thinking Programme (PCTP): 3 studies.
4. Other creative training programmes which combine several essential components of creativity: 10 studies.
5. School programmes trying to improve student's creativity and related abilities through regular class room arrangements: 9 studies.
6. Other long term programmes that use special techniques for enhancing creativity such as creative dramatics, transcendental meditation: 11 studies.

The result of this analysis seem to support the

previous reviews of Torrance (1972) and Parnos and Brunelle (1967). The findings of the study indicate that generally verbal creativity is more affected by these programmes than figural creativity.

The over all results of this meta-analysis suggest that training does affect creativity. It is concluded that creative thinking is skill that can be developed through teaching methodologies and the innate creative thinking ability of individuals can be stimulated and nourished through education and training.

This preview of the earlier reviews provides strong evidence that creativity can be developed through various methods and procedures. A further review in detail will provide us more informations about the different techniques and programmes which have been used to promote creative thinking among children by various researchers during last 25 years in abroad. The discussion will follow in the captions as mentioned earlier.

*Creative Thinking Techniques*

The beginning of research in the area of creativity development was started with the use of creative thinking techniques. These techniques are conscious and deliberate procedures for producing new combination of ideas which help in developing creativity by providing training in creative thinking skill. Some common techniques which have been used by different researchers to develop creative thinking are brain ·storming (Osborn, 1953), attribute listing (Crawford, 1954), morphological analysis (Zwicky, 1957), synectics (Gordon, 1961), checklist (Davis, 1965), role playing (Moreno, 1946; Torrance, 1975), etc.

Parnes and Meadow (1959)[8] used the technique of brain storming for his creative problem solving courses with great success. The effectiveness of this course has been examined in numerous studies involving college and school children.

In an earliest evaluation, Parnes and Meadow (1959)[9] have revealed that on five of the seven measures of creative ability, the student who had taken the one semester course in creative problem solving were significantly superior to the group of matched subjects who had never taken the course.

In another evaluative study, Parnes and Meadow (1960)[10] examined the persistence or carry over effects of the creative problem solving course. Results indicated that the improvement in creative productivity persisted for more than eight months after the completion of the course.

Reese *et al.* (1976)[11] conducted four semester long courses for college students in creative problem solving. Students were divided into experimental and control group. Experimental group were given training in creative problem solving while no training was given to control group students. Each semester emphasized a different aspect of creativity, and effects were assessed at the end of each semester with tests designed to reflect Guilford's structure of intellect. A pre-test battery established the initial comparability of experimental and control students. The training had no significant effect on memory or evaluation operations, but significantly improved divergent production, convergent production, and cognition.

Besides these studies, the use of the technique of brain storming in creative problem solving courses has also been supported in many other research studies (Meadow, Parnes and Reese, 1959[12]; Parnes, 1961[13]; Anderson, 1963[14]; Gray, 1964[15]; Turner and Rains, 1965[16]).

In current years, few more studies have attempted to verify the effectiveness of brain storming technique. Akinoboye (1980)[17] indicated a differential effectiveness of the creativity strategies of brain storming, direct creativity training and problem solving.

Goulub and Hahn (1983)[18] designed a study to compare the effects of a creative training programme on students in both open and traditonal class rooms. During four 30 minutes sessions per week for eight weeks, subjects in the experimental group were trained in brain storming, creative problem solving and the principles for stimulating new ideas. Before and after the training programme, the children were given tests of creativity. The significant differences were found between the control and experimental groups on all measures following exposure to training. Moreover, the gains in creativity were significantly greater for the experimental subjects in the open class room.

Very recently Haley (1984)[19] conducted a study to get the answer of a question "Can the creative expression styles of young children be developed or enhanced by problem solving training". The study concluded that creativity can be taught and the method of training has some differential effects on the quality and quantity of solutions generated in different types of expressions.

In one study, Warren and Davis (1969)[20] compared three techniques of creative thinking, namely, the check list, brain storming and morphological analysis. Subjects were divided in four groups and were given unlimited time to "think of ways to change or improve a door knob". Group-I was taught to use a seven-item check-list with suggested general categories of idea. Group-II used Osborn's idea spuring questions as an idea check list. Group-III was instructed in the morphological synthesis procedure in which ideas for improving one quality of an object are listed along one axis and ideas for improving other qualities along other axis. Group-IV (control) received no instructions regarding techniques. Researchers demonstrated that groups in check list and morphological procedures produced the greatest total number of ideas.

Synectics, a method often used in industry, employs a variety of techniques to facilitate two basic processes: making the strange familiar and making the familiar strange (Gordon, 1961[21], Prince, 1970[22]). The one study evaluating synectics that could be located (Kerth, 1973)[23] achieved limited success with college students. Synectics training significantly enhanced associational fluency, but had no effect on ratings of inventiveness.

The experimental evidences of the research studies reviewed above reveals that creative thinking techniques like Creative Problem Solving, Brain Storming etc. may prove to be an illuminating approach in promoting creative thinking. This observation is in agreement with the conclusion drawn by Torrance (1972)[24] while reviewing the research studies involving different approaches to foster creativity and Rose and Lin (1984)[25] who gave his conclusion on the basis of the meta analysis of various research studies.

*Transcendental Meditation*

Recently, Psychologists and educationists have become interested in studying transcendental meditation (TM) as a facilitator of creativity. It is thought that the anxiety and stress are the prime cause of mental blocks and difficulties which are the barriers in the way of creativity development. Transcendental meditation then becomes one of the several techniques to remove the internal blocks and encourage the flow of this creative energy (Gowan, 1978)[26].

Despite the fact that Transcendental meditation has been current for only a decade or so, a rather sizeable amount of research as to its beneficial effects on creativity has accumulated.

MacCallum (1975)[27] found the Transcendental meditation as an effective procedure to develop creativity among people. The similar results were obtained by Schecter (1975)[28] who found T.M. effective in classrooms. Ferguson (1977)[29] found that the average treatment effect of TM on creativity was almost twice that of any other variable.

Ball (1980)[30] conducted a study to find out the effect of TM sidhis and TM programmes on creativity. The result indicated that the TM sidhis and TM improved the originality of the subjects.

Though only few studies have been conducted with regard to the TM's effectiveness, but it appears that TM programmes can help to promote creative thinking in children. However, before reaching to any definite conclusion, more research is needed in this area.

*Teaching Methods*

The Teaching methods have a vital role in developing pupil's creativity. It has been stressed that methodology of teaching employed and curriculum assignment in a particular class room or school affect the development of children's creativity (William, 1972)[31]. But the research literature in this area reveals that only few attempts have been made to test the effectiveness of various methods of teaching in developing pupil's creativity.

One of the earliest attempt in this direction was made by Sommers (1961)[32] who investigated the feasibility of improving creative thinking within the framework of existing subject matter courses by using "specific methods designed to increase certain creative abilities". The experiment was conducted in an industrial art laboratory type course. Evaluation of the experiment was based on scores yielded by pre and post test of subject matter and creative thinking. The test of imagination (Form DX) prepared by the Bureau of Educational Research at the University of Minnesota was used to evaluate gains in creative thinking. The experimental hypotheses were tested by use of an analysis of co-variance technique. Experimental group were found to have made significantly greater gains in the total creative thinking scores than had the control group.

Possien (1964)[33] evaluated three specific teaching methodologies in terms of their effectiveness in the development of the problem-solving skills of three groups of sixth grade children in the area of map study and interpretation. The 'inductive method', designated as method-A, required the pupils to solve a series of map problems through a process of searching and self discovery. The deductive method, designated as method-B, involved the simple telling of facts and generalizations by the teacher and rote learning by the pupils. Method-C was deductive in nature but detailed explanations of the causal relationships underlying the concepts were added to the lesson plans. The investigator taught each of the three classes for thirty minutes a day for three weeks. The same map and map problems were used for all the three groups. The analysis of data revealed that the inductive method of teaching is more effective as compared to the deductive methods in developing problem solving skills in children.

Jones (1970)[34] studied the effect of teaching strategy in divergent thinking upon the behaviour of student teachers and the children they teach. The study found significant differences for the three factors of the verbal creativity test when children were tested before and after teaching by the teacher.

Johnson (1974) studied the effect of creative teaching upon the creative thinking abilities, achievement and intelligence of selected IV grade children. The results of the various analysis indicated a significant F-ratio in favour of the experimental group on total creative thinking and as well as on flexibility and elaboration.

In an another study Wood (1976)[35] studied the

effects of different teaching styles on creativity. This study shows that there occurs a significant increase in creativity of the children taught by interaction analysis method than for the children educated by traditional method.

Teeling (1979)[36] while studying the effect of Multiple Talent Approach to teaching on the creative thinking performance of elementary students found that this approach favoured the girls as compared to boys on the fluency and flexibility sub-scores and that the fifth grade students scored significantly higher than the third grade students in the experimental group on the fleuency, flexibility and composite score variables.

Besides this, few studies have also been conducted to study the effect of Class room behaviour of teachers on pupils's creativity. Enochs (1965)[37] in a study found that a class room in which pupils can express ideas, ask question, and have their ideas and questions accepted, clarified, or in some way recognized by the teacher, is a class room which promotes pupil's original ideas to a great extent and pupil's flexibility of ideas to a lesser extent.

Recently, Johnes (1980)[38] studied the effect of creativity workshop for teachers upon the class room responding behaviours of teachers towards student's creativity. A class room interaction inventory instrument was developed by the investigator for recording the frequency of each two dimensional creative event—the occurrence of a creative student behaviour and the resulting teacher response. A packet of material was also developed for workshop training sessions. The study indicates the effectiveness of creativity training programme for teachers upon student's creative behaviour.

The above studies show that the teaching methodologies, styles of teaching and classroom teaching behaviour of teachers does affect creativity of children. However, no specific method of creative teaching have been develope l by any of the investigator.

*Instructional Materials*

As mentioned earlier, few attempts have been made to train creativity directly through some specially designed instructional materials. During last two decades, few researchers mostly in U.S.A. have developed some sort of instructional packages to provide children practice and training in the basic skills of creative thinking.

Covington and his associate (1966)[39] designed a "Productive Thinking Programme" for V and VI graders which was further revised in 1974[40]. It is a self-instructional programme consisting of 15 booklets depicting detective type of stories in cartoon format. Instruction is provided in a variety of problem solving skills including both divergent and convergent thinking but with emphasis on the latter. Thus, this programme differs markedly from most other creativity training programmes, which place primary and sometimes exclusive emphasis on divergent thinking.

In an early evaluation using small sample, Covington and Crutchfield (1965)[41] found support for the programme's effectiveness in developing a variety of problem solving skills. Ripple and Dacey (1967)[42] reported less supportive results for a ten lesson version of the programme adapted for VIII graders. Dacey (1971)[43] in a large analysis of the same instructional programme obtained similar results. Equally discouraging results were reported by Treffinger and Ripple (1969[44], 1970[45]) in two separate evaluation studies. However, on an attitude measure, instructed students showed more favourable attitudes towards creative thinking and problem solving than did control students.

Wardrop, Olton, Goodwin, Covington, Kalusmeir, Crutchfield and Ronda (1969)[46] conducted a large evaluation study of the programme involving 704 students from 44 fifth grade classes. A qualified support for the effectiveness of the programme was found in this study, particularly on post test measures that resembled the training material.

Olton and Crutchfield (1969)[47] evaluated the programme under conditions designed to maximize its effectiveness. The 16 basic lessons were supplemented with a set of exercises giving pupils additional experience in productive thinking. It was found that the instructed students scored higher on the post-test and follow-up composite scores.

Moreno and Hogan (1976)[48] reported promising results in a study involving 218 fifth and sixth grade students. Covariance analysis showed that students given the productive thinking programme were superior to controls on all measures of verbal and figural divergent thinking.

Schuler (1974)[49] found less encouraging results as analysis of gain scores yielded no evidence for the effectiveness of the programme, although control student's evaluation scores did show a significant gain.

Recently, Jeanne (1981)[50] conducted an study on educable mentally retarded children by adapting the productive thinking programme to develop creative problem solving skills. Analysis of co-variance with repeated measures were computed using I.Q. as co-variety for each of the creativity measures. The experimental group significantly out performed the control group for the measure of fluency, flexibility and originality for both figural and verbal sub-tests.

Thus, the studies evaluating the productive thinking programme have yielded inconsistent results, with some researchers finding substantial evidence and others finding little such evidence. Nevertheless, these studies provide some evidence that the creativity can be trained through productive thinking programme. Moreover, it must be noted that the largest training effects have often been found in small studies with serious methodological limitations.

Second noteworthy effort to train creativity through some instructional material was made by Feldhusen, Speedie and Treffinger (1971)[51] who developed "Purdue Creative Thinking Programme (PCTP)" for VI grade children. It was designed to foster the divergent thinking abilities of verbal and figural fluency, flexibility, originality and elaboration. It consists of 28 audio-tapes with accompanying printed exercises for providing practice in divergent thinking skills. This programme has been evaluated in number of studies, most of which have been reported in several places.

The first study (Bahlke, 1967[52]; Feldhusen, Bahlke and Treffinger, 1969[53]; Feldhusen, Speedie and Treffinger, 1971[54]) provides only modest support for the effectiveness of the programme and the second study (Behlke, 1969[55]; Feldhusen, Treffinger and Behlke, 1970[56]; Feldhusen, Treffinger & Thomas, 1971[57]) has shown weak evidence for its effectiveness. However, a third evaluation study (Alencer, Feldhusen and Widak, 1976)[58] shows more supportive results in the favour of the programme.

In two studies, the Purdue Creative Thinking Programme has been compared with the Productive Thinking Programme discussed earlier. While one study (Shively, Feldhusen and Treffinger, 1972)[59] shows more effectiveness of Purdue Creative Thinking Programme, the another study (Treffinger, 1971[60]; Treffinger, Speedie, and Brunner, 1974[61]) provides the results just reverse of it.

One another study has evaluated the effectiveness of the PCTP (Huber, Treffinger, Tracy and Rand, 1979)[62]. The investigators have tested the efficacy of the programme with gifted and regular students of fourth, fifth and sixth grade. The results of this study provide limited but significant support for the effectiveness of the programme. The programme was found to be successful in influencing verbal fluency for gifted and regular students in grade 4, 5 and 6.

Recently, Marlene (1983)[63] designed a study to evaluate the divergent component of PCTP and found that the divergent activity component of the programme are effective in the development of creative performance.

In summary, these evaluation studies suggest that Purdue Creative Thinking Programme has, at best, limited effectiveness. The same conclusions have been drawn by Rose and Lin (1984)[64] who found PCTP to have relatively small effects.

The third Creativity Training Programme in this series have been prepared by Myers and Torrance (1964[65]; 1965a[66], 1965b[67], 1966[68], 1966b[69], 1968[70]) who have developed a set of work books designed to foster creativity in elementary school children.

Britton (1967)[71] evaluated one work book "Invitation to thinking" and doing in a study of 330 VI grade students and found that the total verbal and non-verbal scores favoured the trained group, as did a majority of the sub-scores.

In a second study using "Invitations to thinking and doing", Woodliffe (1970)[72] found evidence for the effectiveness of the booklet, but only when it was used in combination with inservice sessions with teachers.

A third study, using the Myers-Torrance work books with trainable mentally retarded children was reported by Cherry (1973)[73]. A group using the work books showed significant gains.

Recently Gloulub and Hahn (1983)[74] used the exercises from Myer's and Torrance's booklets and found significant differences between control and experimental groups following exposure to training.

The paucity of soundly designed research on the Myers-Torrance work books is surprising, considering their popularity. These work books may be effective in improving verbal divergent thinking scores, especially, when teachers are guided in the use of the work books (Mansfield, Busse, Krepelka, 1978)[75].

Khatena (1970)[76] had developed a training material that provides instruction and practice in five creative thinking strategies: (a) breaking away from the obvious and commonplace, (b) transposition, (c) analogy,

(d) re-structuring, and (e) synthesis. He has used different version of the training instrument with adults and children. The duration of training has ranged from two 60-minute session to nine 40-minute sessions. Khatena (1970[77], 1971a[78], 1971b[79], 1973[80]) and Khatena and Dickerson (1973)[81] have reported several evaluations of the training programme. In these evaluation studies, Khatena has presented some evidence for the effectiveness of his training material with both children and adults. The essence of Khatena's training appears to be the provision for practice in producing original responses.

Renjulli (1973)[82] developed 'New Direction in Creativity (NDC) Programme in a more systematic manner. It is in the five volumes (Marks 1, 2, 3, A and B). Each volume of the programme contains 24 types of creativity training activities which have been designed to develop four basic general creative thinking abilities; fluency, flexibility, originality and elaboration. This programme have been evaluated in number of studies.

First evaluation of this programme was done by Callahan and Renjulli (1974)[83] on a limited population (35 classes of six graders were randomly assigned to the experimental group and 28 classes to the control group). The experimental group classes used the material for 2½ hours per week for 8 weeks while the control group continued regular class room activities.

At the end of the 8 weeks period all subjects were administered the verbal Form A and Figural Form B of Torrance test of creative thinking (TTCT). Though, the difference between the experimental and control group was found non-significant statistically, but the higher mean scores of treatment groups showed that the programme may be used to develop creative thinking among children.

Ford and Renjulli (1976)[84] used the 'New Direction in creativity (NDC) programme (Mark 1) for Educable Mentally Retarded (EMR) children. The subjects for this study consisted of 30 groups of middle grade and high school level EMR children. Of these 30 classes, 18 were randomly assigned to the experimental group and the remaining 12 class rooms as the control group. The I.Q. range of the sample population was 50 to 80 and the children ranged from 10 to 16. The experimental group was given training for 12 weeks at the rate of 2 activities per week. A post-test only control group design was used and MANOVA was applied to the data. It was found that NDC programme had the greatest effect on the subject's flexibility, with significant effects on originality and fluency.

Besides these programmes as discussed above, there are some other programmes which have been evaluated only once. A programme developed by True (1966)[85] based on the principles of general sementics, led to increase scores for six graders on measures of ideational fluency and spontaneous flexibility.

Shackel and Lowerance (1969)[86] training high ability 12-years olds achieved success with a programme designed to enhance verbal divergent thinking abilities.

Similarly, Franklin and Richards (1977)[87] found evidence for the effectiveness of a set of activities providing practice in divergent production.

Recently Tweet (1981)[88] investigated the effect of creativity training into the social studies curriculum. Two instructional programmes were developed on the basis of Parnes-Osborn creativity training procedures. One programme placed creativity training into the social studies curriculum. The second programme dispersed creativity training throughout the curriculum. The participant of the study were fifth and sixth grade students. Three comparable groups were selected at each grade level; one group for each programme and one group acting as a non-treatment goup. The instruments used were the Torrance Test of Creative Thinking and the test for inquiry social studies. After the pretesting, five months training was given to two treatment groups which was followed by Post-test. Two way analysis of variance was used to determine whether there were significant interactions between sex or intelligence and teaching methods. The study concluded that (1) student's creativity skills could be increased by either teaching method on the creativity sub-tests for fluency and originality, (2) the social studies skills of students were significantly increased by the procedures which incorporated creativity training into the social studies curriculum, (3) the non-treatment groups generated no significant changes in either social studies or creativity skills, (4) there were no interactions detected between student sex or intelligence and teaching methods.

In studies evaluating these programmes divergent thinking or other creativity tests are typically administered before and after training and the effectiveness of training is assessed by gains on these tests. The review of the related literature evaluating various creativity training programmes seems to support the view that creativity can be trained. However, this optimistic conclusion is pre-mature, since methodological problems pervade most evaluation studies. One of the most important limitation of these evaluation studies has been the use of individual scores rather than group means as the unit of analysis.

*Other Procedures*

Few other procedures which make use of some speical techniques or the combination of various methods of techniques have also tried to facilitate creative thinking.

Nicholson (1959)[89] designed on experiment to determine the effects of a group of training methods upon the creativity. Training methods included (i) lecture and discussion of the main points in "Osborn's Applied Imagination" and accompanying teachers guide; (ii) the "other world" technique of Arnold; (iii) the lecture and discussion of traditional approaches to problem solving; (iv) actual time in brain storming, apart from related Osborn training; (v) training with locally produced materials such as Guilford's Association Test; and (vi) miscellaneous procedures such as Maltzman's "Word Association in Depth" technique. Finding of the study suggests that training by varied methods can be used to bring about a significant improvement in the production of remote or uncommon ideas.

Browers (1965)[90] investigated the effect of hypnosis and suggestions on creativity test performance. It was hypothesized that relaxation through hypnosis and suggestions will help in reducing mental blocks which, in turn, facilitate creative performance. The data indicated that hypnosis can increase test originality.

In one study, Kraft (1979)[91] determined the effect of "Conceptualization training" upon the development of creativity and it was concluded that the conceptualization training can develop creativity in VI grade children.

Boutte (1980)[92] has applied the technique of "Cognitive Behaviour Modification" to enhance pupil's creativity. It was found to be an effective technique for enhancing elaboration. This study recommends that cognitive behaviour modification should be considered as an alternative when trying to enhance elaboration because it appears to be simple, inexpensive, easy to use and could easily be incorporated into class room objectives using a variety of class room materials or simple modifications thereof.

Fults (1980)[93] conducted a study to determine the effectiveness of an instructional programme for developing creative thinking, a positive self-concept and leadership among intellectually and academically gifted elementary students in grade four, five and six. The experimental curriculum was comprised of five major elements (i) provision of time for the intellectually and academically gifted students to work with others of his or her capabilities, (ii) stimulation of individual interests, (iii) provision of enriched experiences, (iv) emphasis on the development of cognitive skills, and (v) emphasis on the development of affective skills. The study reports significant difference between the post-test creativity scores for the experimental group and control group in favour of the former. Girls appeared to benefit more than boys from training in creativity. Training was also found to be more effective for fifth grade children and equally effective for both moderately intellectually gifted and highly intellectually gifted.

Tadlock (1980)[94] designed a "Movement Education Programme (MEP)" and tried it on gifted students of 2nd and 3rd grade. The programme was found to be effective for third graders in the development of three of the four components of creative thinking.

Jackson (1981)[95] investigated the use of open questions and physical interpretation with a traditional curriculum topic of reading and writing poetry as a method of enhancing the creativity of students as evidenced in their creative work. The creativity training programme using the reading and writing of poetry found to be successful in creating significant improvements in student's creativity scores on Torrance Test.

Thus, we find that so many other procedures have been employed by various researchers to promote creative thinking in children. Amost all the studies in this section have shown the effectiveness of their techniques, but unless a particular technique is repeatedly used and more studies are conducted to verify the earlier results, it would not be justifiable to rely their validity at this stage.

**Research Scenario : India**

The research work in this field appears to have received attention only very recently in India. This is evident from the fact that a significant interest in research on the development of creativity was started in India in late seventies, but it began to take visible shape at the turn of eighties only. The review of research literature in India, during last one decade or so, reveals that though few researches have been conducted to develop creativity in children through various procedures, but no serious attempt has been made to promote creative thinking through some systematically designed creativity training programme.

Gupta (1974)[96] surveyed the field of creativity in India and found projects in various stages of completion. A break down of Indian Researches in the field is given below:

**Table 1: Classification on Indian Researches on Creativity in Major Fields (1974)**

| S. No. | Field of Research | No. of Studies | Per cent |
|---|---|---|---|
| 1. | Procees of Creativity | 26 | 34.2 |
| 2. | Creativity in relation to personality | 29 | 38.2 |
| 3. | Creativity in relation to achievement and other similar variables | 7 | 9.2 |
| 4. | Creative Environment | 6 | 7.9 |
| 5. | Creative Product | 3 | 3.9 |
| 6. | Miscellaneous | 5 | 6.6 |

It is apparent from the table that the majority of research has been done in the area of personality as related to creativity and the process of creativity while other important areas remain to be investigated. It is also evident from this survey that no study has been conducted with regard to the development of creativity through training till 1974.

After this whatever little has been done in India in the last one decade or so in the field of creativity development, the investigator has tried to take a stock of it in order to have a deeper insight into the present study. The discussion will follow in the captions as mentioned earlier.

*Creative Thinking Techniques*

Although there are number of techniques to develop creative thinking, but the Indian researchers have tried only four techniques mainly, *viz.*, creative problem solving, brain storming, role playing, and morphological analysis. Out of these four, the first three techniques seem to be more popular.

Raina and Chaturvedi (1970)[97] conducted a study in which high school students were given training in the process of creative problem solving. It was observed that the training significantly improved the pupil's fluency on the Torrance Test of Creative Thinking.

Chatterjee and Mitra (1976) as described by Passi and Jarial (1983)[98], studied the effectiveness of brain storming on the generation of ideas by the adults. Sixty students from the undergraduate classes, with age group 17-18 years were given training in brain storming. It was observed that brain storming proved significantly effective in increasing the quality as well as quantity of ideas. Further, the male subjects improved more on originality than their female counterparts, as a result of training in brain storming.

Gupta (1977) as described by Passi and Jarial (1983)[99], has also attempted to compare the effect of teaching physics to X grade students through brain storming technique and through traditional method of teaching on the creativity of the students. Of the two comparable groups (on the basis of mean scores on creativity factors), one group was taught through the brain storming for 10 consecutive school days, whereas, the other group (control) was taught through the traditional method. Three sub-tests from the Passi tests of Creativity, namely, the seeing problems, the unusual uses and the consequences were used as the measures of creativity. It was observed that the group taught through the brain storming technique obtained higher mean scores only on fluency factor of seeing problems test, but achieved lower mean scores on fluency factor of consequences test than the traditionally taught group.

Nirpharake (1977)[100] designed his study to develop an integrated programme of creativity training based upon the four vital areas of creativity, namely, training in cognition or perception, evaluation and appreciation, divergent production and creative problem solving. The programme was tried on 36 students of VII grade who were divided into six groups of six students in each. The first four groups were assigned to one of the above mentioned four treatments respectively; the fifth group was given training in all the four areas while the sixth group was not given any training in any of the above mentioned strategies. The training consisted of 100 sessions, 25 sessions devoted to each area of creativity. The general procedure was as follows: First, general introduction to the programme and instruction, then short lectures on the principles followed by discussion, demonstration of a technique by the experimenter, exercise on it by subjects individually and collectively again followed by discussion. Using TTCT as the criterion measure, it was observed that all the four strategies, as well as, their combinations proved significantly effective in developing student's creative thinking.

Pillay (1978)[101] conducted a study to find out the effect of "Creative Teaching Method" (Combination of brain storming, morphological analysis and traditional method) upon the several creative thinking abilities and creative thinking in geography of VIII grade students. The study employed a multifactor covariance design "having experimental and control groups". Treatment in the study was the teaching of geography through the creative teaching method. The sample consisted of 71 VIII grade students (36 control group and 35 experimental group).

The results showed that the creative teaching method did not produce differential effect on the general creative thinking abilities of students on the Passi's Test of Creativity, as compared to the traditional teaching method. It did not produce differential effect upon the development of student's creative thinking in geography also. Among the five operations of the "Structure of Intellect" only convergent production ability in geography improved significantly more by the creative teaching method than by the traditional teaching method. Thus, this study showed that the treatment to the students in brain storming and related techniques did not help significantly in the development of creative thinking.

In another study, Deshmukh (1980) as described by Passi and Jarial (1983)[102], studied the effect of brain storming and role playing technique in developing the creative thinking abilities of VIII grade students. The sample of the study consisted of 144 students who were divided into three groups: experimental group-A (N=46), experimental group-B (N=50), and control group-C (N=48). The students of group-A were taught 30 lessons in Marathi and social sciences through the brain storming technique; group-B was taught the same lessons following the role playing technique; and the similar content was taught to the students of group-C through the traditional method of teaching. Using the verbal and figural forms of TTCT as well as their parallel forms at pre and post test stage respectively, it was observed that the technique of brain storming proved significantly effective in developing student's scores on various components of verbal and figural measures of creativity, as well as, on composites creativity, whereas the technique of role playing and traditional method of teaching did not help in the development of creativity. Further, the gains in student's creativity scores were not found to be effected by the variance in levels of intelligence whereas in the brain storming group, females gained significantly higher than males on TTCT. Lastly, the initially low creative students were benefited most by teaching through brain storming and role playing technique, than average and high creative students in terms of their gains on creativity tests.

D'Lima (1981) as described by Passi and Jarial (1983)[103] applied the technique of brain storming for developing creative thinking abilities among the children through the teachers. Sequential brain storming was done by the teacher-trainees on the topic 'Family Planning' to arrive at many ideas through 25 cartoons. The transparencies of these cartoons were again used by the teacher trainees to brain storm the children, so as to improve the cartoons. Although no standard tools were used for assessing the children's responses (behaviours), yet it was concluded that the training in brain storming helped the children significantly to think more original and divergent ideas.

It may be seen from the above review that the five studies have used the technique of brain storming to develop creative thinking abilities of the subjects. Of these, two studies (Gupta, 1977; and Pillay, 1978) have shown that the technique of brain storming does not help significantly in the development of creativity. The results of the other two studies (Chatterji and Mitra, 1976; and D'Lima, 1981) can not be relied upon in the absence of the validity of the tools used by them. Only one study (Deshmukh, 1980) has shown its effectiveness in developing creativity.

In such a state of affairs, no decision can be taken regarding the effectiveness of brain storming in developing creativity with reference to the Indian context. Further investigations with valid instruments and proper experimental procedures are required to conclude upon the effectiveness of brain storming in developing creativity in Indian culture. The techniques of morphological analysis and role playing have been tried in only one study, each by Pillay (1978) and Deshmuk (1980) respectively, but they have not shown their significant effectiveness in developing creativity of the respective samples. Training in Creative problem solving studied in two studies (Raina and Chaturvedi, 1970; Nirpharake, 1977) seems to be more promising as compared to the other technique for developing creativity in school children as both the studies have provided favourable results.

*Transcendental Meditation*

Transcendental Meditation (TM) has been proved effective in developing the higher mental processes including the creative thinking abilities of the meditators in different cultures. It has a wide spread and permanent effect on Physiological, psychological and neurological functioning of an individual. In India, only two studies have so far investigated into the effect of TM on the creative thinking abilities of the subjects.

Of the two studies, one was carried out by NCERT (1980)[104]. As many as 260 male students of class IX, having age range from 14 to 16 years practised the TM for a period of one year. Utilizing the "Experimental control group design", it was observed that the practice in TM helped the students of experimental group to develop their creative thinking abilities significantly higher than that of the control group.

The second study (Sausanwal, Sathe, and Jarial, 1980)[105] investigated the effect of TM on the verbal creative thinking abilities of IX grade female students of 16-10 years of age. Following the "Experimental Control Group Design", 20 students of the experimental group were observed practising the TM twice a day for about a year, whereas the 20 students of the control group had no such practice. Using the Passi's Test of creativity as the criterion measure, it was observed that the fluency and originality components of creativity improved significantly after the practice in TM for five months whereas it took nine months to improve the flexibility component of verbal creativity significantly.

Of the two studies conducted to find out the effect of practice in TM on the development of creativity, both have shown its significance. Although, it may be said tentatively that the practice in TM helps the meditators in improving their creative thinking abilities, yet keeping in view the limited number of studies in this respect, it will be too early to conclude.

*Teaching Methods*

Different teaching methods may have their differential effect upon the mental abilities of students. In this respect one study has been conducted by Prasad (1979)[106] to find out the effect of discovery method of teaching on the creative thinking abilities of students. The study followed a 'pre-test-post-test experimental control group design'. Twenty four students of class IX constitute the sample of the study who were divided in two comparable groups (on the basis of pre-test creativity, intelligence and academic achievement scores). One of these two groups (experimental) was taught physics through the discovery method of teaching whereas the other group (control) was taught similar lessons in physics through the traditional method of teaching. Using the Mehdi Tests of Verbal Creativity as the criterion measure, it was observed that the discovery method of teaching proved significantly effective in developing the fluency, flexibility, and originality dimensions of creativity.

Besides this study, there are some more worth mentioning attempts by the Indian investigators in the task of developing creativity through various teaching methods which are still under progress. As described by Passi and Jarial (1983),[107] Shah (1980) is engaged in experimentally investigating the effect of some selected teaching strategies on the development of creative thinking abilities and academic achievement of secondary school students. Ramkrishnan (1981) has prepared lesson plans based upon the "Willaim's Cognitive Affective Model" for teaching science to IX grade students. Kowdi (1982) is studying the effect of some teaching models for the cultivation of pupil's creativity. The results of these studies are eagerly awaited.

As only one study (Prasad, 1979) has been conducted so far whose findings are available, it would be too early to arrive at any conclusion. However, on the basis of the findings of the research studies conducted abroad, it can be said that methodology of teaching does affect creativity as discussed earlier.

### *Instructional Material*

In India too, few attempts have been made to train pupil's creativity directly through the use of instructional programmes. Only recently, two researchers have prepared instructional material to train creative thinking and both of them have shown the effectiveness of the material with respect of the development of creativity among students.

Jarial (1981)[108] designed his doctoral study with the objective to prepare a programme for developing verbal and non-verbal creative thinking abilities among the students of IX grade. Both the forms of the programme (Verbal and non-verbal) included 25 lessons each. The experimental part of the study followed a 'pre-test - post-test experimental control group design'. The sample consisted of 80 students each for the verbal and non-verbal form of the programme. Each set of 80 students was divided into two comparable (on the basis of IQ scores and pre-test scores of creativity) groups - experimental and control. The treatment given to the students of experimental group (verbal as well as non-verbal) continued for 50 days, utilizing one period per day of 35 minutes duration. The 'Torrance Test of Creative Thinking' (TTCT) was administered before and after the treatment. The results showed a significant effectiveness of the programme in developing different components of verbal creativity (fluency, flexibility, originality and composite creativity) and various components of non-verbal creativity (Fluency, Flexibility, Originality, Elaboration and Composite creativity). The development of the various components of verbal and non-verbal creativity was found to be independent of the effect of sex, socio-economic status and initial creativity levels except in the case of non-verbal elaboration with respect to which the female students and the students of initially low creativity levels gained significantly higher than male students and the students of initially high creativity levels respectively.

Bhaskara (1982)[109] prepared a programme for developing creativity among VI grade students. This programme was based upon the exercises providing training to the children in creativity through puzzles, riddles, consequences, creative problem solving, mystery plots, story writing, poem writing and construction of riddles. The students were given training in the programme for 3 months—utilizing one hour per day for this purpose. Using the "Passi Test of Creativity" and employing the "Single Group Pre-test-Post-test design" the investigator observed that the programme proved significantly effective in developing the mean creativity scores of the students.

Though, the research studies conducted in India studying the effectiveness of instructional material on the development of creativity have shown favourable results, but it would not be justifiable to arrive at any conclusion at this stage keeping in view the limited number of studies as only two studies with this respect have been conducted till to-date. Moreover, the one study (Jarial, 1981) has used the foreign made Torrance Test of Creative Thinking whose appropriateness is doubtful in the Indian context, while the second study, though have used an Indian test to measure creativity but has ignored the non-verbal aspect of creative thinking in its instructional material. It seems that these investigators have not been serious in considering all the aspects in mind. Hence, a depth study is seriously needed with this regard.

## Stock-taking of the Past Researches

The review of the researches in the area of creativity development conducted in India and abroad as discussed in the preceding pages indicates the possibility of developing creative thinking in children through various methods and procedures.

In abroad, though, a large number of studies have been conducted to develop creative thinking among school children thought various methods and procedures, only few attempts have been made to design a creativity training programme for this purpose which make use of some sort of instructional material. Moreover, the studies evaluating these material does not show the consistent results, thus placing the doubt on their validity. How far these instructional material would be valid in Indian situation is further questionable. At this point, it must be mentioned that though the investigator did succeed in gathering the information with regard to the effectiveness of various types of instructional material, but it could not be traced out what type of material the instructional programmes consisted of. Thus, the nature of the instructional material developed abroad is not clear at all, at least to the investigator.

Situation is still worse in India, as only two studies have been conducted which have used instructional material to develop creative thinking among school children. Though both the studies have shown the effectiveness of the material, but it is too early to arrive at any definite conclusion unless some more studies are conducted in this respect. Moreover, these studies can not be relied upon much due to the unclear rationale of the instructional material prepared and methodological limitations of the research design by the researchers adopted. Hence, no decision can be taken regarding the validity of the instructional materials prepared by the researchers in India unless some comprehensive studies based on sound rationale and with serious methodological considerations are under taken in this regard.

**Justification for the Present Study**

From the analysis of the past researches, it seems that no serious attempt have been made in India to develop a comprehensive creativity training programme which make use of a systematically developed instructional material based on sound rationale. Moreover, the past Indian researches have their own limitations in terms of the size of the sample, tools used and methodological problems.

The present study was selected keeping the above consideration in view and thus it departs from the earlier researches in the following way:

(i) The instructional material of the present creativity training programme is based on sound rationale which is discussed in the foregoing chapters.

(ii) The sample selected is large enough on the

basis of which definite conclusion can be drawn.

(iii) To measure the student's creativity, an Indian Test (Baquer Mehdi's Test of Verbal and Non-Verbal Creativity) has been used so as to suit in the Indian context.

(iv) Sex and intelligence of the children have been controlled with the help of experimental design used in the study while age and socio-economic background are partially controlled with the nature of sample selected. The variable of grade level of students is completely controlled of grade level of students is completely controlled as only IV grade students have been considered for the experiment.

(v) To find out the effectiveness of the programme, analysis of variance (ANOVA) of difference measures (gain score) has been used as a statistical technique which taken into consideration the initial scores, thus serving as an alternate to the analysis of covariance.

(vi) Mean gain scores have been taken as a unit of analysis instead of individual scores.

(vii) by using 2×3×2 (Treatment x Intelligence level × Sex) factorial design, the influence of intelligence and sex has also been tested on the effectiveness of the creativity training programme by finding out the interaction effects.

Foot Notes:


1. J.P. Guilford. Creativity. *American Psychologist,* 1950, Vol. 9, pp. 444-454.
2. S.J. Parnes and E.A. Burnelle. The Literature of Creativity (Part I). *Journal of Creative Behaviour.* 1967, Vol. 1, No.l, p. 52.
3. S.J. Parnes; and E.A. Brunelle. The Literature of Creativity (Part I). *Journal of Creative Behaviour.* Winter, 1967, Vol. 1, No. 1, pp. 52-109.
4. E.P. Torrance; and J.P. Torrance. Is Creativity Teachable? Bloomington, Ind. Phi Delta, *Kappan,* Educational Foundation, 1973.
5. R.S. Mansfield, T.V. Busse, and E.J. Krepelka. The Effectiveness of Creativity Training. *Review of Educational Research, Fall,* 1978, Vol. 48, No. 4, pp. 517-536.
6. Laura Hall, Rose and Hsin-Tai, Lin. A Meta-Analysis of Long Term Creativity Training Programmes. *Journal of Creative Behaviour.* 1984, Vol. 18, No. 1, pp. 11-22.
7. G.V. Glass. Intergrating findings: The Meta-Analysis of Research. In Shulman, L.S. (Ed.) *Review of Rosearch in Education,* Itasca, IL: Peacock, 1978, Vol. 5.
8. S.J. Parnes: and A. Meadow. Effects of "Brain Storming" Instructions on Creative Problem Solving by Trained and Untrained Subjects. *Journal of Educational Psychology,* 1959, Vol. 50, pp. 171-176.
9. S.J. Parnes, and A. Meadow. Evaluation of Training in Creative Problem solving. *Journal of Applied Psychology,* 1959, Vol. 43, pp. 189-194.
10. S.J. Parnes, and A. Meadow. Evaluation of Persistence of effects produced by a Creative Problem Solving Course. *Psychological Reports,* 1960, Vol. 7, pp. 357-361.

11. H.W. Reese, S.J. Parnes, D.J. Treffinger and G. Kaltsounis. Effects of a Creative Studies Programme on Structure of Intellect Factors. *Journal of Educational Psychology,* 1976, Vol. 68, pp. 401-410.
12. A. Meadow, S.J. Parnes and H. Reese. Influence of brain storming instructions and problem sequence on a problem solving test. *Journal of Applied Psychology,* 1959, Vol. 43, pp. 413-416.
13. S.J. Parnes. Effects of extended support in creative problem solving. *Journal of Educational Psychology.* 1961, Vol. 52, pp. 117-122.
14. Donald Norris, Anderson. An experimental Evaluation of Two methods for developing creative problem solving abilities in an Industrial Art Course. *Dissertation Abstract International.* 1963, Vol. 24, No. 5, pp. 1934-1935-A.
15. W.W. Gray. An experimental study utilizing the problem solving technique in a IX Grade Heath Class. *Dissertation Abstract International.* 1964, Vol. 25, No. 4, p. 2457-A.
16. W.M. Turner and J.D. Rains. Differential effects of "Brain Storming" instructions upon high and low creative subjects. *Psychological Reports,* 1965, Vol. 17, pp. 753-54.
17. J.O. Akinboye. An Experimental study of the Effectiveness of brain storming in small groups of Nigerian subjects. *Journal of Creative Behaviour.* 1980, Vol. 14, No.1, p. 268.
18. S. Goulub and K.S. Hahn. Training Creative thinking in the open and traditional class rooms. *Journal of Creative Behaviour.* 1983, Vol. 17, No. 3, p. 217.
19. G.L. Haley. Creative Response Styles: The Effects of Socio-economic status and problem solving training. *Journal of Creative Behaviour.* 1984, Vol. 18, No.1, pp. 25-40.
20. T.E. Warren; and G.A. Davis. Techniques for creative thinking: Empirical Comparison of three methods, *Psychological Re-*

*port,* 1969, Vol. 25, No. 1, pp. 207-214.

21. W.J. Gordon. *Synectics.* New York, Harper and Brothers, 1961.
22. G.M. Prince. *The Practice of Creativity,* New York, Harper and Row, 1970.
23. W.L. Kerth. Training in Creative Thinking: The Effect of the Individual of Training in the "Synectics" method of group problem solving. *Dessertation Abstract International.* 1973, Vol. 33, p. 3947-B.
24. E.P. Torrance. Can we Teach Children to Think Creatively? *Journal of Creative Behaviour.* 1972, Vol. 6, pp. 114-143.
25. Laura Hall, Rose and Hsin-Tai, Lin. A meta analysis of Long Term Creativity Training Programmes. *Journal of Creative Behaviour.* Vol. 18, No. 1, 1984, pp. 11-22.
26. J.C. Gowan. The Facilitation of Creativity through Meditational Frocedures. *Journal of Creative Behaviour.* 1978, Vol. 12, No.3, pp. 156-160.
27. M.J. MaCallum. T.M. and Creativity. In Orme-Johnson, D. and Farrow, J.T., *Scientific Research on the T.M. Programme* Vol. 1: Collected Papers. NYC. Maharishi International University, 1975.
28. H. Schecter. The T.M. Programme in the Class room. In Orme-Johnson, D. and Farrow, J.T. *Scientific Research on the T.M. Programme* (Vol. 1: Collected Papers), NYC. Maharishi International University, 1975.
29. P.C. Ferguson. *The Meta Analysis of the Transcendental Programme.* Doctoral. Dissertation, School of Education. University of Colorado, Boulder, 1977.
30. Crlow Fugene, Ball. The Effects of Transcendental Meditation (TM) and the TM sidhis programme on Verbal and Figural Creativity (TTCT), Auditory Creativity and Hemispheric Dominance (SOLAT). *Dissertation Abstract International,* Vol. 40, No. 1, 1980, p. 3880-A.

31. F.E. Williams. *A Total Creativity Training Programme for Individualizing and Humanizing the Learning Process.* Englewood Cliffs. N.J.P. Educational Technology Publications, 1972.
32. W.S. Sommers (1961). The influence of selected Teaching Methods on the Development of Creative Thinking. *Dissertation Abstract International.* 1962, Vol. 22, No. 11, p. 3954-A.
33. W.M. Possien (1964). A Comparison of the Effects of Three Teaching Methodologies on the Development of the Problem Solving Skills of Sixth Grade Children. *Dissertation Abstract International,* 1965, Vol. 25, No. 7, p. 4003.
34. J.C. Jones. A Study of the Effect of a Teaching Strategy in Divergent thinking upon the behaviour of student teachers and children they teach. *Dissertation Abstract International.* 1970, Vol. 30, No. 11, pp. 2231-A.
35. E.J. Johnson. Creative Teaching—Its effect upon the creative thinking ability, achievement and intelligence of selected fourth grade students. *Dissertation Abstract International,* 1975, Vol. 35, No.1, p. 4132-A.
36. Dannis Wood. The effects of different teaching styles on creativity. *Journal of Creative Behaviour,* 1976, Vol. 10, No. 3, p. 220.
37. T. Teeling (1979). The effect of the multi-talent approach to teaching on the creative thinking performance of elementary students. *Dissertation Abstract Internation.* 1980, Vol. 40, p. 3751-A.
38. P. D. Enochs. An experimental study of a method for developing creative thinking in V grade children. *Dissertation Abstract International,* 1965, Vol. 28, No. 8, pp. 4538-4539.
39. Helen, Johnes. The effects of a training programme for teachers upon the class room responding behaviour of teachers

towards creative student behaviour. *Dissertation Abstract International*, 1980, Vol. 41, No. 3, p. 1028-A.

40. M. V. Covington; R. S. Crutchfield; and L.B. Davis. The *Productive Thinking Programme.* Berkeley: Braselton Printing Co., 1966.
41. M.V. Covington, R.S. Crutchfield; L.B. Davis; and R.M. Olton. *The Productive Thinking Programme–A Course in Learning to Think.* Columbus, Chio: Merrill, 1974.
42. M.V. Covington; and R.S. Crutchfield. Facilitation of Creative Problem Solving. *Programmed Instruction,* 1965, Vol. 4, No. 4, pp. 3-5.
43. R.E. Ripple and J. Dacey. The facilitation of problem solving and verbal creativity by exposure to programmed instruction. *Psychology in the Schools,* 1967, Vol. 4, pp. 240-245.
44. J.S. Dacey. Programmed Instruction in creativity and Its effects on eighth grade students (Doctoral Dissertation, Cornell University, 1967), *Dissertation Abstract, International,* 1971, Vol. 32, pp. 2479-A.
45. D. Treffinger; and R.E. Ripple. Developing Creative Problem solving abilities and Related attitudes through programmed instruction. *Journal of Creative Behaviour.* 1969, Vol. 3, pp. 105-110.
46. D. Treffinger; and R.E. Ripple. The Effect of programmed instruction on Creative problem solving and Attitudes. *Irish Journal of Education,* 1970, Vol. 4, pp. 47-59.
47. J.L. Wardrop; R.M. Olton; W.L. Goodwin; M.V. Covington; H.J. Klausmeir; Crutchfield, R.S.; and T. Ronda. The development of productive thinking skills in fifth grade children. *Journal of Experimental Education,* 1969, Vol. 37, pp. 67-77.
48. R.M. Olton; and R.S. Crutchfield. Developing the skills of

Productive Thinking. In P. Mussen, J. Langer, and M. Covington (Eds.) *Trends and Issues in Developmental Psychology*, New York: Holt, Rinehart and Winston, 1969.

49. J.M. Moreno; and J.D. Hogon. The Influence of Race and Social Class Level on the Training of Creative Thinking and Problem solving abilities. *Journal of Educational Research,* 1976, Vol. 70, pp. 91-95.
50. G. Schuler. *The Effectiveness of the Productive Thinking* Programme. Ithaca, N.Y.: Ithaca College, 1974.
51. G. Jeanne. Developing the Creative Problem Solving Skills of intermediate age educable mentally retarded children. *Dissertation Abstract International,* 1981, Vol. 41, No. 2, p. 3495-A.
52. J. F. Feldhusen; S.M. Speedie; and D.J. Treffinger. The purdue creative thinking programme-Research and Evaluation. *National Society for Performance and Instruction Journal,* 1971, Vol. 10, No. 3, pp. 5-9.
53. S. J. Behlke. *A Study of the Enhancement of Creative Abilities in Elementary School Children.* Unpublished Master's Thesis. Purdue University, 1967.
54. J.F. Feldhusen; S.J. Bahlke and D.J. Treffinger, Teching Creative Thinking. *Elementary School Journal,* 1969, Vol. 70. pp. 48-53.
55. J.F. Feldhusen; S.M. Speedie; and D.J. Treffinger. The Purdue Creative Thinking Programme - Research and Evaluation. *National Society for Performance and Instructiòn Journal,* 1971, Vol. 10, No. 3, pp. 5-9.
56. S.J. Bahlke. Componential Evaluation of Creativity Instructional Materials. *Dissertation Abstract International,* 1969, Vol. 30, pp. 1426-A.
57. J.f. Feldhusen; D.J. Treffinger and S.J. Bahlke. Developing Creative Thinking: The Purdue Creativity Programme. *Jour-*

*nal of Creative Behaviour,* 1970, Vol. 4, pp. 85-90.

58. J.F. Feldhusen; D.J. Treffinger; and S.J. Thomas. *Global and Componential Evaluation of Creativity Instructional Materials.* Buffalo, New York: The Creative Education Foundation, 1971.
59. E. Alencer; J.F. Feldhusen; and F.W. Widlak. Creativity Training in Elementary Schools in Brazil. *Journal of Experimental Education.* 1976, Vol. 44, No.4, pp. 23-27.
60. J.E. Shively; J.F. Feldhusen; and d.J. Treffinger. Developing Creativity and Related Attitudes. *Journal of Experimental Education,* 1972, Vol. 41, pp. 63-69.
61. D.J. Treffinger. *Improving Children's Creative Problem Solving Abilities: Effects of Distribution of Training, Teacher Involvement and Teacher's Divergent Thinking Ability on Instruction.* Final Report; office of Education. Indiana, Purdue University, 1971.
62. D.J. Treffinger; S.M. Speedie; and W.D. Brunner. Improving Children's Creative Problem Solving Ability: The Purdue Creativity Project. *Journal of Creative Behaviour.* 1974, Vol. 8, pp. 20-30.
63. J. Huber; D. Treffinger; D. Tracy and D. Rand. Self-Instructional use of Programmed Creativity Training Material with Gifted and Regular Studies. *Journal of Educational Psychology,* 1979, Vol. 71, No. 3, pp. 303-309.
64. S.Z. Marlene. Effect of an Instrumentional Programme and Teacher's Verbal Praise on the Creative Performance of IV Grade Children. *Dissertation Abstract International.* 1983, Vol. 44, No. 6, p. 1689-A.
65. Laura Hall, Rose and Hsin-Tai, Lin. A meta analysis of Long Term Creativity Training Programmes. *Journal of Creative Behaviour,* 1984, Vol. 18, No.1, pp. 11-22.
66. R.E. Myers; and E.P. Torrance, *Invitation to Thinking and*

*Doing.* Boston, Massachusetts: Ginn, 1964.

67. R.E. Myers; and E.P. Torrance. Can You Imagine? Boston, Massachusetts: Ginn, 1965a.
68. R.E. Myers; and E.P. Torrance. *Invitation to Speaking and Writing Creatively,* Boston, 1965(b).
69. R.E. Myers; and E.P. Torrance. *For those who Wonder.* Boston, Massachusetts: Ginn, 1966(a).
70. R.E. Myers; and E.P. Torrance. *Plote, Puzzles and Plays,* Boston, 1966(b).
71. R.E. Myers; and E.P. Torrance. *Strech,* Boston, 1968.
72. R.J. Britton (1967). A Study of Creativity in Selected Sixth Grade Groups. *Dissertation Abstract International,* 1968, Vol. 28, p. 3546-A.
73. H.M. Woodliffe. *A Study of* Change in the Creative Thinking Ability in Fifth Grade Children. *Unpublished Doctroal Dissertation,* University of Toronto, 1970.
74. B.S. Cherry. A strategy for developing creative thinking (Torrance Model) in trainable mentally retarded children and open ended methods. *Dissertation Abstract International,* 1973, Vol. 33, pp. 4975-4976-A.
75. Sharon Gloulub and Karen Sorci Hahn. Training Creative Thinking in the Open and Traditional Class room. *Journal of Creative Behaviour,* 1983, Vol. 17, No. 3, p. 217.
76. R.S. Mansfield; T.V. Busse; and E.J. Krepelka. The Effectiveness of Creativity Training. *Review of Educational Research,* 1978, Vol. 48, No. 4, pp. 517-536.
77. J. Khetena. Training College Adults to Think Creatively with words. *Psychological Reports,* 1970, Vol. 27, pp. 279-281.
78. J. Khatena. Training College Adults to think creatively with words. *Psychological Reports,* 1970, Vol. 27, pp. 279-281.
79. J. Khatena. A Second study training college adults to think

creatively with words. *Psychological Reports,* 1971, Vol. 28, pp. 385-386(a).

80. J. Khatena. Teaching Disadvantaged Pre-school children to think creatively with pictures. *Journal of Educational Psychology.* 1971, Vol. 62, pp. 384-386(b).
81. J. Khatena. Creative level and its effects on training college adults to think creatively with words. *Psychological Reports,* 1973, Vol. 32, p. 336.
82. J. Khatena; and E.C. Dickerson. Training sixth grade children to think creatively with words. *Psychological Reports,* 1973, Vol. 32, pp. 841-842.
83. J.S. Renjulli, *New Directions in Creativity,* New York, Harper and Row, 1973.
84. C.M. Callahan and J.S. Renjulli. Development and Evaluation of a Creativity Training Programme. *Exceptional Children,* 1974, Vol. 38, pp. 44-45.
85. B.J. Ford, and J.S. Renjulli. Developing the Creative Potential of Educable Mentally Retarded (EMR) Students. *Journal of Creative Behaviour.* Creative Education Foundation, Inc., 1976, Vol. 10, No.3, pp. 210-218.
86. S.A. True. A Study of the Relation of General Sementics and Creativity. *Journal of Experimental Education,* 1966, Vol. 34, pp. 34-40.
87. D.S.J. Shackel and P.J. Lawerence. Improving Creativity through Programmed Instruction. *New Zealand Journal of Educational Studies,* 1969, Vol. 41, pp. 63-69.
88. B.S. Franklin; and P.N. Richards. Effects on Children's Divergent Thinking Abilities of a Period of Direct Teaching for Divergent Production. *British Journal of Educational Psychology,* 1977, Vol. 47, pp. 66-70.
89. Claudia Clague-Tweet. The Effects of the Implementation of Creativity Training in the Elementary School Social Studies

Curriculum. *Journal of Creative Behaviour,* 1981, Vol. 15, No. 1, pp. 70-71.

90. P.N. Nicholson. An experimental Investigation of the effects of Training upon Creativity. *Dissertation Abstract International.* Vol. 20, No.3, p. 1071-A.
91. P.G. Browers. Effect of Hypnosis and Suggestions of Reduced Defensiveness on Creativity Test Performance. *Dissertation Abstract International,* 1965, Vol. 26, No. 5, pp. 2864-65-A.
92. M.B. Kraft. Conceptualization Training: For Creativity and Academic Achievement. *Dissertation Abstract International,* 1980, Vol. 40, p. 3895-A.
93. Margaret, Boutte. The effects of Cognitive Behavour Modification on Enhancing Creativity, *Dissertation Absract International,* 1980, Vol. 40, p. 5783-a.
94. Elizabeth Ann, Fults. The Effect of an Instructional Programme on the Creative Thinking Skills, Self Concept and Leadership of Intellectually and Academically Gifted Elementary Students. *Dissertation Abstract International.* 1981, Vol. 41, No. 7, p. 2931-A.
95. Sharon Elaine, Tadlock. The Effect of a Basic Movement Education Programme on the Creative Thinking Skills and Self-Concept of Gifted Students. *Dissertation Abstract International,* 1980, Vol. 41, No. 6, p. 3407-A.
96. W.S. Jackson. Creativity Training's Effect on Poetry writing. *Dissertation Abstract International,* 1981, Vol. 42, No. 5, p. 2047-A.
97. A.K. Gupta. Creativity Research in India - Its Past and Future. *Creativity News Letter,* 1974, Vol. 3, pp. 18-24.
98. M.K. Raina, and S. Chaturvedi, (1970). Effects of Training in Creative Problem Solving on Fluency of Thinking. *Indian Journal of Applied Psychology,* 1970, Vol. 7, pp. 71-

74.

99. B.K. Passi and G.S. Jarial. Research on Creativity Training in India: A Review. In Govind Tewari and Roma Pal (Ed.), *Status of Indian Researches in Creativity.* Agra Psychological Research Cell, Agra, 1983, p. 48.
100. B.K. Passi and G.S. Jarial. Research on Creativity Training in India: A review. In Govind Tewari and Roma Pal, (Editors), *Status of Indian Researches in Creativity,* Agra Psychological Research Cell, 1983, p. 48.
101. A.M. Nirpharake (1977). An experimental study of some methods of training. In M.B. Buch (Editor) *Second Survey of Research in Education.* Centre for Advanced Studies in Education, M.S. University, Baroda.
102. G.S. Pillay (1978). Effects of Patterns of Teaching Upon Creative Thinking Among Adolescents. In M.B. Buch (Ed.) *Second Survey of Research in Education,* Centre for Advanced Studies in Education, M.S. University, Baroda.
103. B.K. Passi and G.S. Jarial. Research on Creativity Training in India: A Review. In Govind Tewari and Roma Pal (Eds.). *Status of Indian Researches in Creativity.* Agra Psychological Research Cell, Agra, 1983, p. 49.
104. B.K. Passi and G.S. Jarial. Research on Creativity Training in India: A Review. In Govind Tewari and Roma Pal (Eds.). *Status of Indian Researches in Creativity.* Agra Psychological Research Cell, Agra, 1983, p. 50.
105. NCERT (1980). TM enhances creativity in students, NCERT news letter, New Delhi, July-Sept. 1980, Vol. VI, Nos. 8-10.
106. D.N. Sausanwal, S. Sathe, and G.S. Jarial. Facilitation of Creative Thinking Abilities Through Transcendental Meditation. *Journal of Indian Education,* Sept., 1980, Vol. VI, No. 3, pp. 9-13.

107. V. Prasad. Promotion of Creativity and Achievement by Discovery Method. *Indian Education Review*, Oct., 1979, Vol. XIV, No. 4, pp. 85-89.

108. B.K. Passi and G.S. Jarial. Research on Creativity Training in India: A Review. In Goving Tewari and Roma Pal (Editors), *Status of Indian Researches in Creativity*. Agra Psychological Research Cell, Agra, 1983, p. 52.

109. G.S. Jarial. Instructional Material for developing creativity in IX grade children. *Unpublished Doctoral Dissertation*, Indore University, Indore, 1981.

110. S. Bhaskara (1982). Study of the Effectiveness of verbal Creativity Instructional Material at school stage. *Unpublished Ph.D. Dissertation*, M.S. University, Baroda, 1982.

# three

## DEVELOPMENT OF CREATIVITY TRAINING PROGRAMME

It has already been discussed that creativity in school children is capable of being developed through appropriate education and training. A major problem that has hamphered efforts to promote creative thinking in class room has been the shortage of appropriate instructional material in this area, particularly in the Indian context. In this part of the present study, an attempt has been made to systematically develop a "Creativity Training Programme (CTP)" that will help children to learn a variety of ways for expressing their creative potential. The whole development of the programme is discussed in the following steps:

### Nature of the Programme

Creativity training programme to be developed as a part of this study refers to a set of instructional material that contains within it systematically organized learning activities for developing creative thinking in children.

Creativity is a dynamic process that involves "a way of looking at things", therefore the activities included in this programme are designed to broaden the way that children look at their world. The programme is not an end itself, but rather a stories of first steps that will provide children with the basic skills involved in creative production.

Further, it is to be noted that this programme is not exactly based on the Skinner's theory of programmed learning in true sense where the bits of knowledge are arranged in a sequence logically. In this programme each exercise is independent of the others. However, it does take into consideration one of the basic concept of feedback where students are made aware of the possible answers of a particular exercise. Therefore, a key of the programme has also been prepared.

In last, it must be made clear here that this creativity training programme as a tool does not intend to measure any trait like other tools. Rather, it is a tool to provide children only the training in developing their creative thinking skills.

**Purpose of the Programme**

Since one of the basic assumptions underlying the present study is that all people possess the ability to think creatively in varying degrees, the main purpose of the programme is to assist the children in generating responses that are creative for the individual student at his present level of mental functioning. It is of course hoped that such experiences in creative thinking at their own level will help students develop a characteristic way of looking at things that will ultimately result in the creation of ideas and products that are truely original and useful for the culture at large.

With this purpose in mind, the programme is designed to develop each of the following creative thinking abilities:

(a) Fluency,

(b) Flexibility,

(c) Originality,

(d) Elaboration.

Thus, the programme aims at providing a set of experiences that are systematically and purposefully dire-cted towards the development of above mentioned creative thinking abilities. However, it is to be noted that the programme is not offered as the only approach to this problem, nor is it maintained that the programme will develop all of the many dimensions of creativity that seem to exist. Rather, it is offered as one possible approach to creativity training that has been developed within a specified framework. This framework has been discussed in the proceeding pages.

## Assumptions Underlying the Programme

The creativity training programme prepared for the present study is based on the following assumptions:

(a) Creative thinking can be developed without making major changes in the basic cognitive capacities of the student. Instead of developing entirely new and different cognitive capacities, such instructional material can be prepared and used which help the children to make the effective use of the cognitive capacities he already had (Olton, 1968)[1].

(b) Creative thinking abilities can be strengthened by giving students exercises similar to the tests measuring the particular abilities. It can be assumed that if the number of responses to a particular test is a good indicator of fluency ability, then the use of the same tests as exercises might strengthen this ability (Guilford, 1962)[2].

This view is further supported by Steinmetz (1965)[3] who has described how the modifications of Torrance's battery to test creativity is used as a teaching device in a sales training programme. He finally concludes that the Torrance Test could even be used easily and profitably by teachers to train salesman to think creatively.

(c) As the gerenal creative thinking abilities, namely,

fluency, flexibility, originality and elaboration are closely related with the abilities of divergent production slab of Guilford's Structure of Intellect (Guilford, 1967)[4] the exercises can be prepared on the basis of various types of intellectual activities involved in the operation of divergent thinking. Thus, each ability factor of divergent production slab can be taken as a base to prepare an exercise which can help to promote one or more of these four general creative thinking ability, if the students are given practice on it.

(d) Most of the children are unable to show their creative performance, because they don't know, 'how to think creatively'. If the students are explained the various ways and steps which are involved in creative thinking and are asked to use them by solving creative thinking exercises, it can be expected that they would be able to think in more creative ways than otherwise.

(e) Creative behaviour can be programmed (Parnes, 1967)[5]. In other words, it is possible to introduce training for creative performance by means of some kind of modified programmes. Crutchfield and Covington (1965)[6] is of the opinion that programmes can be written in such a way that the student is called upon to use and to develop a rich diversity of creative thinking skills.

## Principles Underlying the Programme:

The programme developed for the present study is based on the following principles as given by Renjulli[7]

*Fluency of thought*

Fluency of thought is an important condition for creative production (Renjulli, 1973)[8]. Guilford once said, the person who is capable of producing a large number of ideas per unit of time, other thing being equal, has a greater chance of having significant ideas. In more simple words, the persons who produce a large number of ideas are more likely to produce ideas that are more original. Thus, the fluency principle which underlies the development of this creativity training programme, maintains that fluency is necessary, though not sufficient condition for originality.

Thus, each exercise in this programme attempts to capitalize on the fluence principle by including the number of exercises that generate a large number of responses. Further, in each exercise, the students are first provided with a problem that has many possible alternative solutions and then they are encouraged to write down all their thoughts and ideas that come to mind, no matter how silly or wild the ideas may be.

*Open-ended exercise*

In traditional class rooms, teachers usually raise problems that have one pre-determined solution and students are rewarded for the speed and accuracy with which they converge on the solution. Such exercises provides students with very limited opportunities to let their minds reach accross a broad range of possible solutions to a given problem (Renjulli, 1973)[9].

The exercises in the present programme are based on the principle that when the students are given open-ended exercises on different problems, they get the opportunity to generate many possible solutions to that problem. To meet out this purpose, the exercises in the programme have been prepared in such a way that students don't have to give any pre-determined right or wrong responses. In this way, the students are given opportunity to generate many possible solutions to a particular problem.

Thus, we can help children to become more creative thinkers by giv.ng them numerous opportunities to practice on material which allows for many acceptable responses (Renjulli, 1973).[10]

*Unevaluated Practice*

When children are encouraged to express themselves in an open-ended manner as described earlier, it is extremely important that we also provide them with a climate that is free from external evaluation and the critical judgement so often associated with the traditional school work. Students should be given opportunity to work in an free atmosphere without the constant threat of failure or being wrong.

Therefore, if we want the students to produce as many ideas as they can, it is of utmost importance to value quality and withhold criticism and evaluation until students have exhausted their total supply of ideas related to a given problem (Renjulli, 1973)[11]. This is known as the principle of unevaluated practice. Torrance (1965)[12] has shown that when children work under conditions of un-evaluated practice and are encouraged to experiment freely, they generally display higher levels of creative performance on subsequent occasions than do individuals who work under conditions of evaluated practice.

Thus, the main purpose of un-evaluated practice is to free children from the fear of making mistakes so that they can produce number of ideas. Keeping this in mind, no grading system have been prepared for the programme. Without any threat of imposed evaluation, students work freely on the various exercises.

*Self-Evaluation*

The most effective way to help children think in a creative way is to lead them in the direction of self-evaluation. Therefore, one of the principle of the programme is to help students learn how to evaluate their own creative products. In traditional school instruction, students almost look to the teacher for evaluation and approval; and by so doing, they fail to develop a desire for self-evaluation.

Based on this principle, the programme so developed by the investigator also presents the key of the possible solutions of the various exercises. Students after solving an exercise can go through its possible answers and thus can evaluate themselves.

*Environmental Relevancy*

When students are engaged in creativity training, they should not be penalized for a lack of knowledge about a particular topic. In other words, creativity training activities should allow the learner to draw open his own back ground and experiences. Unless these activities are relevant to a student's present background and immediate environment, the exercises are likely to become traditional search-for-information experiences. Thus, it is important in creativity training to develop exercises that are based on information that is relatively common to all the members of a group.

Considering this principle in mind, the programme has not been prepared on any particular subject area where the content knowledge is involved. Rather, the exercises have been prepared on the areas of general concern related to the immediate environment of the child.

## Theoretical Framework of the Programme

The theoretical framework of the "Creativity training

programme (CTP)" to be developed by the investigator for the present study is based on the Guilford's Structure of Intellect Model (Guilford, 1959). This model has been viewed by many educators as a potentially powerful tool for bringing about needed changes in the curriculum. A brief overview of this model will provide us with the necessary frame of reference for understanding the approach used in this creativity training programme.

As shown in the figure 1, the structure of intellect model is a three dimensional classification system that is designed to organized 120 possible human abilities according to the type of:

(a) mentoal operations employed in an act.

(b) contents involved in the thinking process.

(c) products that result from the act of thinking.

Guilford has distinguished five operations, four content and six products as given below, each being designated by a code letter.

*Operations*:

(i) Cognition (C)
(ii) Memory (M)
(iii) Divergent production (D)
(iv) Convergent production (N)
(v) Evaluation (E)

*Content*:

(i) Figural (F)

Figure 1: Digramatic Refpresentation of Guilford's structure of Intellect Model

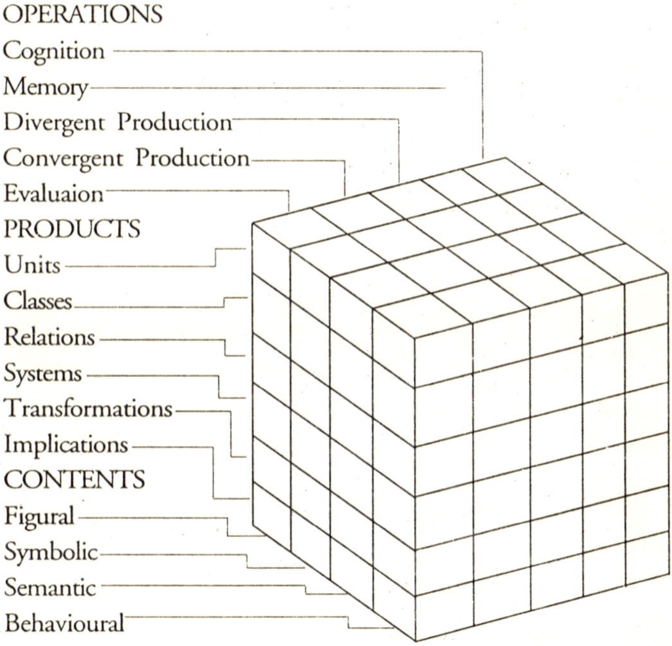


(ii) Symbolic (S)

(iii) Sementic (M)

(iv) Behavioural (B)

*Product:*

(i) Unit (U)

(ii) Class (C)
(iii) Relation (R)
(iv) System (S)
(v) Transformation (T)
(vi) Implication (I)

*Operation:* It indicates the mental process performed in processing the information with which we come into contact. There may be the following five types of mental operations.

Cognition is the mental process which involves recognition of information in various forms. Understanding and comprehension are terms that are commonly used to describe the act of cognition.

Memory is the process of generating information or storage of information. This operation represents the simple reproduction of facts, formulæ, or other items recognized and remembered contents through use of certain processes, like rote memory etc.

Divergent production is the process of generating information from the given information, where the emphasis is on variety quantity and relevance from the same source. It involves scanning stored information, thinking in different directions, searching for many possible solutions, etc. According to Guilford, the divergent thinking abilities are the abilities of productive thinking domain and are closely related to creativity.

Convergent production is the process of generating information from given information, where the emphasis is on achieving the conventionally accepted outcome. It involves finding the correct solution to a problem by manipulating the given information. This is also thought of belonging to the production thinking domain. Intelligence is supposed to be the ability of convergent thinking type.

Evaluation is the mental operation that refers to reaching decisions or making judgements about information. This is a continuous process of judging every product for its validity and has a logical base. Whenever comparisons are to be made between two contents, they are weighed through this process. It requires correctness, suitability, adequacy, determination of fit and so on.

*Contents:* It is type of information to which the mental process is applied. There may be the following four broad classes of informations which are termed as contents.

Figural content consists of information in concrete form as perceived through senses in the form of images like shapes, diagrams etc. It is represented by geometrical patterns and designs.

Symbolic content involves information in the form of signs that have no significance in and of themselves. It is represented by letters, numbers or other conventional signs. Its information is abstract.

Sementic content is information in the form of verbal meaning or ideas as conveyed by some language. It provides more meaningful information to us. Sementic material is the major element in verbal thinking.

Behavioural content consists of essentially non-verbal information that is involved in human interactions, such as the awareness of attitudes, needs, desires, moods, intentions, perceptions and thoughts of other persons and of ourselves. The identification of abilities involving this type of content has not been as precisely defined as those abilities involved in figural, symbolic and sementic content.

*Products*: The product dimension is a form that information takes when it is processed by the human mind. The following six types of products may result when a particular type of mental operation acts upon a particular content material.

Units are relatively segregated or circumscribed items of information that have singular character. Thus, it is the product in the form of an individual item or thing. For example, 'mango' is a unit representing a specific quality of a thing by which name it is distinguished.

Classes are recognized as sets of units of information grouped together by virtue of their common properties. Thus, a class includes many units, each unit though distinguishable from each other can be grouped with other units having a common characteristic. For example, 'fruit' is a class.

Relations are recognized as connections between units of information based on variables or points of contact that apply to them. For example, a chair and desk would constitute a relation.

Systems are organized or structured aggregates of units of information that are grouped together because of the interrelatedness or interaction of their respective parts. Systems are essentially combinations of units, classes and relations that have some total function. Thus, it provides configurational quality among different parts. For example, 'School' is a system.

Transformations are changes of various kinds of existing or known information. It involves the redefinition or modification of existing ideas, products or materials.

Implications consist of extrapolations of information in the form of expectancies, predictions, known or suspected antecedents, commitments, or consequences. For example, asking questions answer to which should help us see a particular problem more clearly, suggests implications from known information.

When the three cross classifications as mentioned above are combined in the three-dimensional model, the intersection of a certain kind of operation, a certain kind of content and a certain kind of product, give rise a certain kind of ability which is represented by a single cell. Thus, combination of 5 operations, 4 contents and 6 products give rise 5 × 4 × 6 = 120 mental abilities, each ability being represented by a separate cell whose properties can be stated in terms of three category concepts to which the ability belong.

Guilford has used various single letters to represent these three facets; and abilities by a symbol of three letters showing the three characteristics of the three facets. Thus, if divergent production (D) combines with the sementic content (M), it give rise six products as follows - DMU, DMC, DMR, DMS, DMT and DMI. Each symbol of three letters shows a separate ability factor which is represented by a separate cell.

It is on the basis of this "Guilford's Structure of Intellect Model" as described above the investigator got a theoretical framework of the creativity training programme to be developed for the present study which is explained as given below:

(a) The investigator considered the abilities involved in the operation of divergent thinking as the base for preparing the various exercises of the present creativity training programme as Guilford (1967)[13] believed that the four basic creative thinking abilities (*viz.*, fluency, flexibility, originality and elaboration) are closely related to the abilities of divergent production.

(b) Though the divergent production slab or 'Guilford's structure of Intellect' involves twenty four mental abilities (as shown in Figure-2), the investigator has considered only twelve abilities of sementic (verbal) and figural (non-verbal) content as the abilities under behavioural content has not yet been identified and the abilities under symbolic content and as also of behavioural content are not measurable by the creativity test used in this study.

On the basis of this theoretical framework of the programme as discussed above, the various exercises in the programme are classified according to:

(i) the type of information involved in each exercise (sementic and figural), and

(ii) the ways that the information is organized in each exercise (units, classes, relations, systems, transformations and implications).

Thus, based on this classification the investigator has designed twelve lessons which involve the following twelve intellectual abilities:

a. Divergent production of sementic units (DMU)
b. Divergent production of sementic classes (DMC)
c. Divergent production of sementic relations (DMR)
d. Divergent production of sementic systems (DMS)

e. Divergent production of sementic transformations (DMT)
f. Divergent production of sementic implications (DMI)
g. Divergent production of figural units (DFU)
h. Divergent production of figural classes (DFC)
i. Divergent production of figural relations (DFR)
j. Divergent production of figural systems (DFS)
k. Divergent production of figural transformations (DFT)

**Figure 2: Diagramatic Representation of the Divergent Production Slab of Guilford's Structure of Intellect**

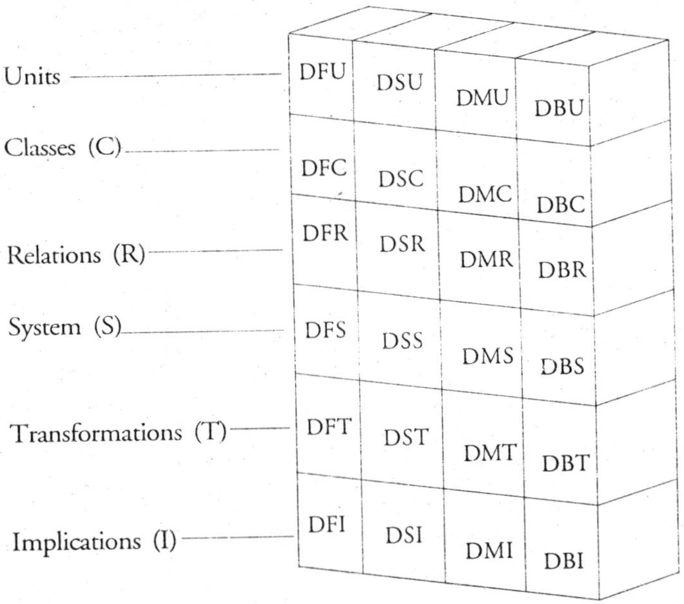

l. Divergent production of figural implications (DFI)

The first six abilities pertain to the verbal creativity while next six to non-verbal creativity as they are based on the sementic (verbal) and figural (non-verbal) content respectively.

**Description of the Programme**

The instructional programme developed by the investigator is designed in the form of a book under the title 'Creativity Training Programme' (CTP). It is prepared in Hindi language as the investigator decided to conduct this study in a Hindi speaking zone of the country. The programme is presented in the following sequence.

(a) *Preface:* The programme beings with a preface in few words for the students to introduce them about the purpose of the training and the content of the book.

(b) *Introduction to the programme:* The preface is followed by the introduction to the programme. It describes the concept and importance of the creative thinking and explations the students "How to Think Creatively'. The purpose of this part is to arouse curiosity in children and to make them ready for undergoing training in creative thinking.

(c) *Instructions:* After the introduction is over, the student are given detailed instructions in the use of the programme. Here, students have been explained in simple language about how to solve various exercises of the programme and how to proceed from one exercise to another.

(d) *Lessons and Exercises:* Just after the instructions, the actual training begins through various exercises in different lessons. In total, twelve lessons have been prepared. First six lessons have been devoted to verbal creative thinking with four exercises in each. Next six lessons are for non-verbal creative thinking and contain three exercises in each. Thus, there are forty-two exercises in total.

(e) *Key to the Exercises:* A key of the various exercises have also been prepared. It contains the possible answers of the various exercises of the programme.

The details of the various lessons and the exercises included in them is given below:

Lessons Number with code Exercise number with title

| | |
|---|---|
| 1. DMU | 1. Leisure Time Utilizaiton. |
| | 2. Waste Paper Utilization. |
| | 3. Thinking of Birth Day Gift. |
| | 4. Thinking of Summer Season. |
| 2. DMC | 1. Situation and Thought. |
| | 2. Thinking of Objects. |
| | 3. Thinking of Digits. |
| | 4. World of Children. |

| | |
|---|---|
| 3. DMR | 1. Synonymous Words. |
| | 2. Antonymuous words. |
| | 3. Related Things. |
| | 4. Sentence Completion. |
| 4. DMS | 1. Fun with letter. |
| | 2. Talking in Poetry. |
| | 3. Let's think of Slogans. |
| | 4. Let's think of Motto's. |
| 5. DMT | 1. What will happen if ..... |
| | 2. Advertisement. |
| | 3. Changing size. |
| | 4. Thinking of Improvement. |
| 6. DMI | 1. A Message from Moon. |
| | 2. Men from Moon. |
| | 3. Lottery. |
| | 4. Future Forecast. |
| 7. DFU | 1. Geometrical Figures. |
| | 2. Word Drawing. |
| | 3. Play with Figures. |
| 8. DFC | 1. Circle based Design. |
| | 2. Rectangle based Design. |
| | 3. Triangle based Design. |
| 9. DFR | 1. Figural Symbolization of thoughts. |
| | 2. Figural Symbolization of Games. |
| | 3. Figural Symbolization of Shapes. |
| 10. DFS | 1. Figure combination. |
| | 2. Letter combination. |
| | 3. Dotted figure. |
| 11. DFT | 1. Picture completion. |

2. Picture construction in Digits.
3. Picture construction in Letters.

12. DFI
1. Picture construction in elliptical figures.
2. Picture construction in rectangular figures.
3. Picture decoration.

The general plan for sequencing the various lessons and exercises takes account of the level of difficulty and logical relationship between certain exercises. The lower level lessons deal with the information that is organized into units, classes, or relations. The higher level lessons deal with the information that is organized into systems, transformations and implications. Various exercises in each lesson are further sequenced according to the difficulty level. In each lesson, the first exercise is more easier than the second and so on. This sequencing is, however, only suggestive and this sequence has been adopted for its own convinces. In actual practice, the students may feel free to modify the sequence according to their interest.

### Designing the Exercises

Before discussing the procedure for preparing the various exercises, firstly, it is to be noted that none of the exercises in the programme are prepared as 'pure exercises' in the divergent production factor under reference, because Guilford's (1967)[14] factor-analytical data has also shown that certain activities are related in varying degree to more than one factor. For this reason, the classification of exercises which is based on the Guilford's Structure of Intellect is intended to point out the major focus of the respective activities in the programme but these classifications should not be interpreted to mean that other abilities are not involved in a given exercise. However, each exercise in the programme is prepared in such a way that it is likely to sample out most of the characteristics of the intellectual operation involved under reference.

Secondly, the nature of the various exercises prepared is almost the same as to the tests measuring the particular creative thinking ability, except few modificaitons in its presentation. Reason for this has been made clear in the preceeding pages of this chapter while discussing the assumption underlying the programme.

Keeping these two thinking in mind, the following procedure has been adopted in preparing the various exercises.

*Study of Test Activities*

At first, the investigator studied thoroughly the various divergent production activities used by the Guilford in his Test Battery for the Analysis of Intelligence in his Aptitude Research Project (Guilford and Hoepfner, 1971)[15]. This gave an idea, what constitute a particular activity and how it measures that particular ability. The study of these activities provided the investigator a rationale for preparing various exercises based upon them.

*Selection of Material*

As the programme was to prepare for developing general creative thinking, it was decided to have the material of general nature pertaining to the general awareness of children at VI grade level because of the reason as discussed earlier in this chapter. Thus, the programme does not concentrate on a particular subject matter rather it touches all the areas of general concern.

The material of the exercises in the verbal form of the programme me that is from lesson first to six was taken from the student's immediate environment *viz.*, home, school, society and some well known scientific discoveries.

The material of the exercises in the non-verbal form of the programme that is from lesson seven to twelve was taken in the form of geometrical figures (such as points, lines, triangles, quadrilateral, curve, circle), Devnagri and Latin alphabets, number and object sketches etc.

*Preparing the Exercises:*

After deciding about the material, the various exercises for each factor of divergent production (in sementic and figural content) were prepared on the basis of the intellectual operations involved for that particular ability factor. While preparing each exercise, the intellectual activity measuring the particular ability by Guilford Test Battery were kept in mind. Exercises were designed in such a way that it sample out most of the characteristics of the intellectual operation involved under reference. Further each exercise was so prepared that it involved two to five activities to be performed by the students.

*Presentation of the Exercises:*

The presentation of the exercises is based on the three basic laws of Thorndike's theory of learning *viz.*, law of readiness, law of practice and law of effect. Thus each exercise involves the following steps which take into consideration the above mentioned laws:

**Step-I:** In first step, a problem is posed before the children in simple language.

**Step-2:** In the second step, some cues to the problem are given in the form of one or two possible answers. This makes them ready to think in the right directions. (Law of Readiness).

**Step-3:** In the third step, students are asked to write down their responses in the space given for each activity of the exercise. (Law of Practice).

**Step-4:** In the fourth step, the students are directed to check their answers with the other possible answer given in the key. It serves two purposes. First, students get satisfaction that their way of thinking is right as they find that most of their answer are of the same type as given in the key. In this way, children get some sort of feed back to proceed further. Secondly, after going through the possible answer given in the key, children get an idea about what other types of answers they must have thought which they could not. It stimulates them for further thinking and they take use of it in answering the next exercise (Law of Effect).

**Step-5:** Children starts solving the next exercise. They are asked to use their experience which they had in solving the previous one.

These five steps have been shown in the diagram in the form of flow chart (Fig. 3). Although, the formate of the activities in the various exercises attempts to take account of the developmental level of the VI grade children, but the open-ended nature of creativity training activities has provided an opportunity to develop a truely non-graded programme which may be used with students at other grade level also *viz.*, VII or VIII or even higher grades.

As, there are no "right" or "wrong" answers, each student can write his answer without any fear of being wrong. Moreover, he can also set his own level of response according to his ability. The responses of bright children may be of higher degree of fluency, flexibility, originality and elaboration, but even the slowest child may be able to respond in a way that is appropriate to his own development level. Thus, one of the major features of this creativity training programme is that children can respond to each ac-

**Fig. 3: Flow Chart Showing the Various Steps Involved in the Presentation of Exercises**

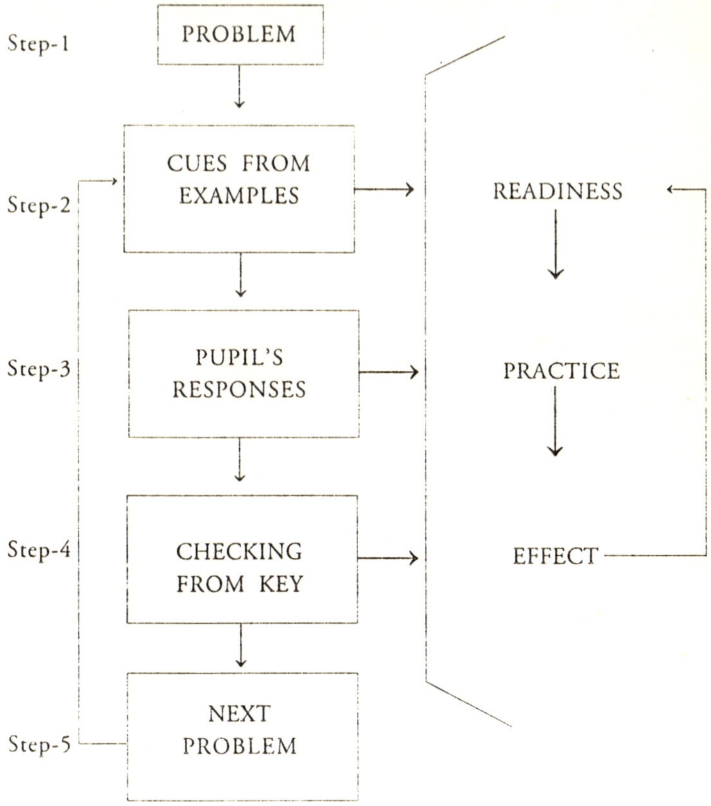

tivity in terms of his own background and experience. Because the programme is not based on the student's ability to recall factual information, each student can be given an opportunity to express his creativity by drawing on his own knowledge and experience.

An effort has also been made to help the children to grasp the main idea of the problem by providing simple explanation and illustrative examples for most of the exercises. It helps the children to start on the right track.

*Preparing a key to the Exercises of the Programme*

After designing the various exercises of the programme, a key to the exercises of the programme was also prepared. It contains the possible answers for each of the exercise of the various lessons. These were arranged in the same order as the programme.

Before the programme was finally made ready for experimentation, it was decided to find out the suitability of the programme in terms of the language in general and in terms of the material and difficulty of the exercises in particular.

For this purpose, the programme was given to 20 students (10 Boys and 10 Girls) of VI grade students selected randomly from one of the school (not included in the actual sample) of the town. As the objective of this administration was not to test the effectiveness of the programme, the students were asked to point out their difficulties in understanding the programme and in answering the various exercises.

On the basis of the student's reactions the following changes were made in the programme:

(a) Some of the exercises which were difficult to understand were modified.

(b) Material of some of the exercises was slightly changed in order to suit their grade level.

(c) Minor changes in language and sentence construction of some of the exercises were made.

## Face Validation of the Programme

As the programme was prepared mainly to provide training to the children in certain creative thinking skills and not to measure any trait, it does not have any grading system so as to provide any date as already pointed out earlier in this chapter. It is due to this reason, it was thought appropriate to find out only the face validity of the programme.

Face validity, here, refers not to what the programme actually does, but to what it appears superficially to do. It pertains to whether the programme "looks valid" to achieve its objective or not. As the objective of the programme is to develop certain creative thinking skills in children, the face validity may help us to tell whether the programme appears to develop those skills which the investigator desires to develop. Moreover, it can also give an idea about how far the programme is suitable to the students for whom it is prepared.

For this purpose, the investigator constructed a "CTP Rating Scale" consisting ten statements to have the opinion of the experts on the programme. This scale had the four point descriptive continuous and the experts were asked to rate their opinion on each statement. The investigator collected the opinion of about 20 experts and the percentage of opinion for each point on the ten statements were determined. All the statements alongwith the obtained opinion (in percentage) at each point of the scale is given below:

**Table 1: Showing the Expert's Opinion on the Creativity Training Programme (CTP)**

1. Do you think that the introductory lesson which explains 'How to think creatively' would be helpful for the students to think of solutions of the exercises in a creative way?

| | | | |
|---|---|---|---|
| Nil | 10% | 30% | 60% |
| Not all all | a bit | quite a lot | very much |

2. Do you think that the exercises presented in the various lessons of the CTP would be able to provide training in the basic skills of creative thinking?

| | | | |
|---|---|---|---|
| Nil | 15% | 40% | 45% |
| Not all all | a bit | quite a lot | very much |

3. How far the exercises in each lesson are representative of the type of divergent production abilty (DPA) involved under reference?

| | | | |
|---|---|---|---|
| Nil | 10% | 50% | 40% |
| to 'No' extent | to some extent | | to quite a |
| to a great | | | |

4. Do you think that pupil's ability to think creatively will improve

after they undergo training through this programme?

| | | | |
|---|---|---|---|
| Nil | 10% | 40% | 50% |
| Not at all | a bit | quite a lot | very much |

5. How far the exercises presented in the various lessons would be able to develop the four basic skills of creative thinking in children?

| | | | |
|---|---|---|---|
| Nil | 5% | 50% | 45% |
| to 'NO' extent | to some extent | to quite a good extent | to a great extent |

6. Do you think that the students after getting training through this programme would be able to produce more original ideas whenever needed?

| | | | |
|---|---|---|---|
| 5% | 65% | 20% | 10% |
| Not at all | a bit | quite a lot | very much |

7. Are the exercises suitable for the VI graders in terms of the material presented?

| | | | |
|---|---|---|---|
| Nil | 5% | 25% | 70% |
| Not at all | some what | quite | very much |

8. Is the programme suitable for the VI graders in terms of the language?

| | | | |
|---|---|---|---|
| Nil | Nil | 20% | 80% |
| Not at all | some what | quite | very much |

9. Are the exercises suitable for VI graders in terms of the difficulty?

| | | | |
|---|---|---|---|
| Nil | 5% | 20% | 75% |
| Not at all | some what | quite | very much |

10. Do you think that if the students are given feed back (after each exercise) in the form of possible answers, it would help them in thinking creatively while solving the next exercise?

| | | | |
|---|---|---|---|
| Nil | 10% | 25% | 65% |
| Not at all | a bit | quite a lot | very much |

From the Table 1 it is revealed that:

I. A large number of experts (60 per cent) felt that the introductory lesson which explains 'how to think creatively' would be very much helpful for the students to think of solutions of the exercises in a creative way. However, few experts (10 per cent) also felt that it would help only a bit while 30 per cent experts found it helpful quite a lot.

From the above opinion of the experts, it seems that the introductory lesson of the creativity training programme (CTP) may be quite helpful for the students to think creatively.

II. Only 45 per cent experts were of the opinion that the exercises in the various lessons of the CTP would very much be able to provide training in the basic skills of creative thinking. Almost same number of experts (40 per cent) gave the opinion 'quite a lot' to this question. However, few experts (15 per cent) found it beneficial only a bit.

It appears that the exercises presented in the various lessons of CTP would certainly be able to provide training in the basic skills of creative thinking.

III. On the question 'how far the exercises in each lessons are representative of the type of divergent production ability (DPA) involved under reference', a good number of experts (50 per cent) found the exercises representative upto quite a good extent and 40 per cent experts to a great extent. However, there were few experts

(10 per cent) who found the exercises representative only to some extent.

With these reactions of the experts, it looks that the exercises, by and large, are representative of the type of divergent production ability involved under reference.

IV. About half the number of the experts (50 per cent) found that the pupil's ability to think creatively will very much improve after the students undergo training through this programme. Though, there were few experts (10 per cent) also who found it helpful in this regard only a bit, but at the same time 40 per cent excerpts have given the opinion that the training will improve pupil's ability to think creatively quite a lot.

It seems that the training programme may be helpful in improving student's ability to think creatively with quite satisfactory degree of success.

V. Though 45 per cent experts found that the exercises would be able to develop the four basic skills of creative thinking in children to a great extent, but 5 per cent were also of the opinion that the exercises will be helpful in this regard only to some extent. However 50 per cent of experts found it beneficial to quite a good extent. Thus, it appears that the exercises, by and large, would be able to develop the four basic skills of creative thinking in children.

VI. The opinion of the experts with regard to the question "Do you think that the students after getting training through this programme would be able to produce more original ideas whenever needed", was not found much encouraging. As much as 65 per cent experts have given the opinion 'a bit' only. Not only this, 5 per cent experts have even felt that the training will not help at all in producing more original ideas whenever students wanted. However, 20 per cent experts were also of the opinion that the training would be able to help quite a lot in this regard. Only 10 per cent experts found the training beneficial very much in this connection.

It seems that the training may not be very much helpful to the students in the long run so that they can produce original ideas whenever needed. However, the positive opinion of some of the experts indicates that it may help, though not in long run.

VII. The exercises of the programme have found very much suitable in terms of the material presented to the 70 per cent of experts, though 5 per cent experts have also found it suitable only some what, while 25 per cent of experts felt it quite suitable in this regard.

Thus, it appears that the programme is very much suitable in terms of the material presented.

VIII. Most of the experts (80 per cent) found the programme very much suitable in terms of the language used. The rest of the experts (20 per cent) were also of the opinion that it is quite suitable.

Programme seems to be very much suitable as far as the language used is concerned.

IX. Majority of the experts (75 per cent) found the exercises very much suitable in terms of the difficulty. However, there were few experts (5 per cent) who felt it some what difficult, 20 per cent experts have given the opinion that it is quite suitable.

It looks that the programme, by and large, is very much suitable for VI graders in terms of the difficulty.

X. Lastly, quite a good number of experts (65 per cent) felt that if the students are given feedback (after each exercise) in the form of possible answers, it would very much help them in thinking creatively while solving the next exercises. About 25 per cent experts have found it helpful quite a lot. However, there were 10 per cent experts who felt it helpful only a bit.

Thus, it appears that if the students are given feed back (after each exercise) in the form of possible answer, it would help them in thinking creatively while solving the next exercise.

With these opinion of the experts, it seems that, by and large, the creativity training programme would be quite valid in developing creative thinking abilities of the students for whom it is prepared.

Foot Notes:

1. R.M. Olton. A Self Instructional Programme for developing Productive Thinking Skills in V and VI grade children. *Journal of Creative Behaviour,* 1968, Vol. 3, No. 1, p. 16.
2. J.P. Guilford. Creativity: Its Measurement and Development. In Parnes, S.J. and Harding, H.F. (Eds.) *A Source Book for Creative Thinking,* New York, Scribner, 1962, pp. 151-158.
3. C.S. Steinmetz. (1965). Creativity Training—A testing Programme that became a sales training programme. In Davis, Gary, A. and Scott, Joseph, A. (Eds.) *Training Creative Thinking,* Holt, Rinehart and Winston, Inc., 1971, pp. 162-171.
4. J.P. Guilford. *The Nature of Human Intelligence,* New York: McGraw Hill, 1967.
5. S.J. Parnes (1967). Programming Creative Behaviour. In S.J. Parnes and E.A. Brunelli. *The Literature of Creativity (Part I). Journal of Creative Behaviour,* 1967, Vol. I, No. 1, p. 86.
6. M.V. Covington and R.S. Crutchfield. Facilitation of Creative Problem solving. *Programmed Instruction,* 1965, Vol. 3, No. 4, p. 234.
7. Joseph S. Renjulli. *New Directions in Creativity,* New York. Harper and Row, 1973, pp. 1-10.
8. Joseph. S. Renjulli. *New Directions in Creativity.* New York, Harper and Row, 1973, pp. 1-10.
9. Joseph S. Renjulli. *New Directions in Creativity.* New York, Harper and Row, 1973, pp. 1-10.
10. Joseph. S. Renjulli. *New Directions in Creativity.* New York, Harper and Row, 1973, pp. 1-10.
11. E.P. Torrance. *Rewarding Creative Behaviour.* Englewood Cliffs. New Jersey, Prentice Hall, 1965.
12. J.P. Guilford. *The Nature of Human Intelligence.* New York,

McGraw Hill, 1967.
13. J.P. Guilford. *The Nature of Human Intelligence.* New York, McGraw Hill, 1967.
14. J.P. Guilford, R. Hoepfner. *The Analysis of Intelligence,* McGraw Hill Book Company, New York, 1971, pp. 367-497.

# four

## RESEARCH DESIGN

After discussing the research problem, the present chapter is devoted to the research design of the study which has been discussed under the following heads:

**Method of the Study**

The selection of a research method depends upon the nature of the study and the objectives to be achieved. As the present study is designed to test the effectiveness of the "Creativity Training Programme (CTP)" upon the development of creative thinking in school children, it involves the conduct of an experiment whereby the effect of treatment can be observed under control conditions.

Therefore, the present study has employed the experimental method of research as it involves the deliberate operation of the treatment conditions by the investigator. In contrast to descriptive method which simply observes the conditions as they occur naturally, the experimental method actually sets the stage for the occurrence of the factor whose performance is to be studied (Kaul, 1984).[1]

Thus, in the present study, the effect of "Creativity training Programme" has been tested by conducting an experiment. For this purpose, the total sample is divided in two equivalent groups *viz.*, Treatment and non-treatment. Treatment group was given training through "Creativity Training Programme" while non-treatment group had no such training. Administering Creativity Tests before and after treatment, the effectiveness of the creativity training programme has been assessed by analyzing statistically the gain scores on these tests. The detailed description of the conduct of this experiment will follow in the foregoing pages.

**Experimental Design**

As the objective of the present study is to test the effectiveness of a "Creativity Training Programme (CTP)" on the development of creative thinking of students and as also its interaction with intelligence and sex, the investigator has employed a "three-dimensional (2 × 3 × 2) factorial design" for the analysis of data as out-lined by dward (1971)[2].

Factorial design is the structure of research in which two or more independent variables are juxtaposed in order to study their independent and interactive effects on a dependent variable (Kerlinger, 1978)[3]. It is because of this reason that the factorial design is selected as the study involves three independent variables (*viz.*, treatment conditions, intelligence level and sex) and a host of dependent variables (*viz.*, measures on the various components of creativity), each being taken separately.

An out-line of the design is given below:

(1) Two treatment conditions: Factor-A.

(i) Training through CTP: Factor-$A_1$.

(ii) No training: Factor-$A_2$.

(2) Three Levels of intelligence: Factor-B.

(i) High level of intelligence: Factor-$B_1$.

(ii) Average level of intelligence: Factor-$B_2$.

(iii) Low level of intelligence: Factor-$B_3$.

(3) Sex: Factor-C.

(i) Male: Factor-$C_1$.

(ii) Female: Factor-$C_2$.

The design is represented diagramatically in the following table. Further, the same design was used for each dependent variable separately.

In the above table, the three letters symbol (like $A_1B_1C_1$, $A_1B_1C_2$, $A_2B_1C_1$ ........ etc. and so on) represents the main gain measures (on the dependent variable under study) of the students belonging to the particular level of intelligence, sex and treatment conditions. For example, the symbol $A_1B_1C_1$ represents the main gain score of the male students belonging to the high intelligence level under treatment group.

Table 1: Diagramatic Representation of the Research Design

| | Sex | Treatment Group (Training Through CTP) | Non-Treatment Group (No Training) |
|---|---|---|---|
| | | ($A_1$) | ($A_2$) |
| High Level of | Male $C_1$ | $A_1B_1C_1$ | $A_2B_1C_1$ |
| Intelligence ($B_1$) | Female $C_2$ | $A_1B_1C_2$ | $A_2B_1C_2$ |
| Average Level of | Male$C_1$ | $A_1B_2C_1$ | $A_2B_2C_1$ |
| Intelligence ($B_2$) | Female $C_2$ | $A_1B_2C_2$ | $A_2B_2C_2$ |
| Low Level of | Male $C_1$ | $A_1B_3C_2$ | $A_2B_3C_1$ |
| Intelligence ($B_3$) | Female $C_2$ | $A_1B_3C_2$ | $A_2B_3C_2$ |

## Population and Sample

As pointed out in the delimitations of the study, all the VI grade students studying in the Hindi medium schools of Haldwani Municipal area (in the district Nainital of U.P.) constitute the population for the present study. Only those schools were considered in the population which were run by the Government. There were two such schools (one boys school and another girls schools) in the town with 188 VI grade girls students and 169 VI grade boys students respectively. The public schools and co-educational schools were not the part of the target population.

In the beginning all the 357 students (188 girls and 169 boys) from the two schools (Government Girls Inter College and Government Boys Inter College) were included in the sample. As both these schools are run by the government, the sample ensures the representation of students from all the sections of the society.

Both the schools had four sections in each. For assigning the students to the treatment and non-treatment group, sections were taken in clustes so as to avoid administrative problems. Two sections from each school were randomly assigned the treatment group and the other two sections the non-treatment group. The position of the total sample of VI grade students in different groups is shown in the following table:

**Table 2: Showing the Position of the Total Sample in the Treatment and Non-Treatment Group Sexwise**

| | Treatment Group | Non-Treatment Group | Total |
|---|---|---|---|
| Girls | 95 | 93 | 188 |
| Boys | 84 | 85 | 169 |
| | 179 | 178 | 357 |

## Tools Used

After selecting the sample, the next step was to choose suitable tools in order to achieve the objectives of the study. The selection of tools for a particular study depends upon various considerations such as the objectives of the study, the amount of time at the disposal of the researches, availability of suitable tests according to Indian conditions, financial resources, and the like. Taking these factors into considerations, the following tools were used in the present study:

(i) Jalota's Group Test of General Mental Ability

to measure the intellectual level of the students.

(ii) Baquer Mehdi's Verbal Test of Creative Thinking to measure verbal fluency, flexibility, originality and composite verbal creativity.

(iii) Baquer Mehdi's Non-verbal Test of Creative Thinking to measure figural originality, elaboration and composite non-verbal creativity.

(iv) Creativity Training Programme (CTP) to provide training to the students in creative thinking (developed by the investigator) and a CTP rating scale to get the experts opinion on the creativity training programme so developed. Rating scale was also prepared by the investigator.

(v) CTP questionnaire to find out the opinion of the students towards the creativity training programme after they undergo training. This too was prepared by the investigator.

The details of the aforesaid tools have been discussed in the foregoing pages.

### *Jalota's Group Test of General Mental Ability*

This is the most widely used test by the researchers in India. This test is constructed by Jalota (1964)[4] specifically for the children of Hindi speaking area. This test has been used only to stratify the sample in the three groups of high, average and low level of intelligence. For this purpose, this test is quite suitable.

*Description*

The test measures the general intelligence level of the children. It comprises 100 verbal type of items. The test includes seven types of items as given below:

(i) Vocabulary similarities.

(ii) Vocabulary opposite.

(iii) Number series.

(iv) Classification.

(v) Best answers.

(vi) Inferences.

(vii) Analogies.

All the items of the test are arranged according to their objectively determined order of difficulty.

*Administration*

The test is very easy to administer. Instructions and examples are given in the beginning of the test. The time limit for the test is 20 minutes.

*Scoring*

For scoring, the test provides the scoring key. Score of each individual is the sum of the right answers. Scoring sheet is also available for this purpose.

Reliability and Validity:

The lower limit of reliability coefficient of the test has been reported to be 0.93 and its concurrent validity coefficients ranged from 0.50 to 0.78.

*Applicability*

This test can be used for the children from VI to X grade in the age group of 11 to 16 years.

***Baquer Mehdi's Verbal Test of Creative Thinking***

This test is developed by Baquer Mehdi (1973)[5] on the lines of Torrance Test of Creative Thinking (TTCP), keeping in view the Indian conditions. Moreover, it is most popular test among Indian researchers owing to its suitability in Indian context. It measures the four components of creativity *viz.*, fluency, flexibility, originality and elaboration.

*Description*

This test includes four sub-tests as given below:

(i) Consequence test.

(ii) Unusual uses test.

(iii) Similarity test.

(iv) Product Improvement test.

Description of these tests alongwith the rationale for their inclusion in the test is given in the manual.

*Administration*

Manual provides a detailed procedure for administering the test. It is recommended that the test administrator should first get himself fully acquainted with the test by carefully going through the test booklet. Though the preliminary instructions to be given to pupils are recorded on the test ,booklets, it is advised to explain the instructions to the students clearly in a simple language. Separate instructions are also given for each activity of the test.

The total time required for administrating the best is 48 minutes, in addition to the necessary for giving instruction, passing out booklets and collecting them back.

*Scoring*

As there is no right or wrong responses for the test much care has to be exercised at the time of scoring. For this purpose, a detailed procedure for scoring is given in the manual. Each item is to be scored for fluency, flexibility and originality. Manual provides a scoring guide for carrying out the scoring of the responses. A separate scoring sheet is also available to summarize the scores for fluency, flexibility and originality. This scoring sheet has the columns for total fluency, total flexibility and total originality scores also.

*Reliability and Validity*

The test-retest reliabilities of factor scores and total

verbal creativity score are reported as follows:

| Fluency | Flexibility | Originality | Total Verbal Creativity Score |
|---|---|---|---|
| .945 | .921 | .896 | .959 |

The validity coefficient against the teacher ratings for each factor and total creativity scores are reported as follows:

| Fluency | Flexibility | Originality | Total Verbal Creativity Score |
|---|---|---|---|
| 0.4* | 0.32* | 0.34* | 0.39* |

* Significant beyond. 01 level.

Reliabilities and validity coefficients for factor score and total creativity score are high enough to place confidence in the use of the test.

*Applicability*

The test is applicable for all age groups and also for rural and urban sample.

*Baquer Mehdi's Non-verbal Test of Creative Thinking*

This test is also developed by Baquer Mehdi (1973)[6] as a part of the total battery which consists of both verbal and non-verbal tests. This non-verbal test of creative thinking is intended to measure the individual's ability to deal with figural content in a creative manner. Thus, it provides the scores on figural (non-verbal) originality, figural (non-verbal) elaboration and composite figural (non-verbal) creativity.

*Description*

The test uses three types of activities for this purpose as given below:

(i) Picture construction.

(ii) Picture completion.

(iii) Triangles and ellipses.

The description of these activities alongwith the rationale for their inclusion in the test is given in the manual.

*Administration*

The procedure of administering the test is same as of Mehdi's verbal test of Creative Thinking. Detailed instructions are given in the manual. Test booklet also provides general instructions and separate instruction for each activity.

The total time required for administering the test is 35 minutes, in addition to the time necessary for giving instructions, passing out booklets and collecting them back.

*Scoring*

Like verbal test, much care has to be taken at the time of scoring as this test also does not have right or wrong responses. Manual provides a detailed procedure for scoring. Each item is to be scored for elaboration and originality. A separate scoring sheet is available to summarize the scores for elaboration and originality. This scoring sheet has the columns for total elaboration and total originality scores also.

*Reliability and Validity*

The test-retest reliabilities of the factor scores and also total non-verbal creativity score are reported as follows:

| Elaboration | Originality | Total Non-Verbal Creativity Score |
|---|---|---|
| .932 | .947 | .946 |

The validity coefficients against the teacher ratings for each factor and the total non-verbal creativity scores are reported as follows:

| Elaboration | Originality | Total Non-Verbal Creativity Score |
|---|---|---|
| .346 | .329 | .385 |

Reliabilities and validity coefficients for factor score and total creativity score are high enough to place confidence in the use of the test.

*Applicability*

The test is applicable for all age groups and also for rural and urban sample.

***Creativity Training Programme (CTP):***

This was the main tool of the study which was prepared by the investigator himself to provide training to the students in creative thinking. The details of this programme have already been discussed in chapter three. A CTP rating scale to get the exper's opinion on Creativity Training Programme was also developed.

*CTP Questionnaire*

A questionnaire to find out the pupil's opinion towards the CTP was also prepared by the investigator himself. It consists of ten statements. Each statement is consisted of two or three possible responses. Students are required to tick mark against any one of the given responses for each statement.

**Variables Involved**

The present study involves two kinds of variables as given below:

(a) *Dependent Variable*

The dependent variables in this study were student's performance scores on various components of creativity which were obtained by the Baquer Mehdi's Verbal and Non-verbal Test of Creative thinking. Thus, the study involves seven dependent variables as given below:

(i) Verbal fluency.
(ii) Verbal flexibility.
(iii) Verbal originality.
(iv) Composite Verbal creativity.
(v) Non-verbal originality.
(vi) Non-verbal elaboration.

(vii) Composite non-verbal creativity.

(b) Independent Variables:

The study involved three independent variables as given below:

(i) Treatment Conditions (CTP Vs No-Treatment).

(ii) Intelligence level (High Vs Average Vs Low).

(iii) Sex (Male Vs Female).

**Execution of the Experiment**

The execution of the experiment and the collection of data for the present study was spread over 28 days from the first week of Jan. 84 to the first week of Feb. 84. Out of these 28 days, the training programme continued for 22 days using one period of 40 minutes on each day. Thus, students received training for more than 14 hour on CTP during data collection.

As already mentioned in the preceding pages while discussing the sample, the principals of the two concerned schools (one boys and one girls) from which the sample for the present study was drawn were intimated well in time about the testing and training programme proposed to be carried out by the investigator. They were interested enough to spare a period every day for about a month. In one school, the period of meeting with the students was kept in the morning while in another school it was kept in the afternoon so that the investigator could visit both the schools every day. Thus, the investigator had two shifts on each day. Before starting the testing and training programme, the investigator collected the lists of the names and class roll numbers of all the students of both the two schools. On the basis of these lists, students were allotted different groups as already discussed in the sample. After this, procedure followed in the steps as given below:

(i) *Administration of Intelligence Test (Jalota's Test of General Mental Abilities)*

On the first day, the students were explained about the purpose of the investigator's meeting with them and thereafter Jalota's Groups Test of General Mental Ability was administered to all the boys and girls students of the sample in two shifts. All the directions and instructions were followed as given in the manual.

(ii) *Administration of Pre-tests (Baquer Mehdi's Verbal and Non-verbal Tests of Creative Thinking)*

On the second and third day, Baquer Mehdi's Verbal and Non-verbal tests of creative thinking were administered on the total sample of the students and the pre-test data was collected in two consecutive days.

The total time required for administering the verbal and non-verbal tests was 48 and 35 minutes respectively, in addition to the time required for giving instructions, passing out booklets and collecting them back. But as the duration of the period was only 40 minutes, the concerned teachers of the class were requested to spare some of the time of their next period also on these particular two days. Moreover, in actual practice the administration of these two tests took about 60 and 45 minutes respectively.

(iii) *Administration of the Creativity Training Programme*

After the administration of pre-test, the actual treatment (*i.e.*, training through CTP) on the students of treatment group was started on the next day which continued for 22 days. Students were given one period of 40 minutes on each day. Thus, the treatment took more than 14 hours in total. Each day, the investigator had two shifts for this purpose, one in the boys school and another in the girls school. The students of the non-treatment group were not given any training. These students continued their studies as usual in that period by their respective teachers.

On the first day of the training, all the students of treatment group were distributed a copy of the Creativity Training Programme and they were asked to write down their name, class etc., in the last page of the programme meant for this. After this, the students were directed to open the first page and read the preface. The contents of the preface were also explained by the investigator himself so as to make them clear about what is to be done. It took about 10 minutes.

After the investigator found that all the students are clear about how to proceed, they were directed to go through the introductory lesson which explains - what is Creative Thinking and how to think creatively. Students were asked to read each line very carefully and with full attention so that they can understand the content which will help them in solving the various exercises of the programme. After the students completed the reading, they were asked to point out any thing which they could not understand. As students were found shy in telling their difficulties, investigator thought it appropriate to read each paragraph loudly before the students and explain them para by para. This was followed by question and answer from both sides which further helped the students to understand more clearly about what is creative thinking and how to think creatively. It took about 20 minutes. This introductory lesson gave an understanding to the students about the importance of creative thinking in human life as well as idea about the process of creative thinking. Investigator observed that the students were quite curious to undergo the training in creative thinking through this programme. May be that this curiosity and readiness among the students was developed due to the introductory lesson.

When it was found that all the students are ready

to undergo the training, the investigator asked them to turn the next page and go through the instructions carefully which explains—how to proceed on the various exercises of the programme. Here, almost all the students raised a question that they are not given the 'Key to the Programme' as mentioned in the instruction. Though in the beginning the investigator had thought to give a copy of the 'Key to the Programme' to all the students, but later on it was decided that only the investigator will keep a copy with him so that the students don't see the possible answer before solving the exercise and instead they can be told about the possible answer when they complete one exercise. The same was explained to the students also. The students were quite convinced about this. At this stage, the work of the day was over.

Next day, all the students were asked to solve two exercise in a period of 40 minutes, spending 20 minutes for each exercise. Though, the time limit was kept fixed on account of the fixed time available at the disposal of the investigator, but in actual practice there was no hard and fast rule and the students were left free to complete the exercise even at home if they find the time short. For this purpose, students were allowed to take the copy of the programme at home and work out whenever they get time. It helped them very much. Work began with the first exercise of the first lesson. After the 20 minutes were over, the investigator told them all the possible answers of the exercise from the 'Key to the Programme'. Here, they were asked to see what other answer they would have thought which they could not.

Now the students were asked that they can write more possible answers (besides what they have been told from the key) for this exercise at their home and start solving the next exercise. Again after 20 minutes, the investigator told them all the possible answer of the second exercise and they were again asked to see what other possible answers they would have thought which they could not. Work of this day was over here. All the students were given their copy of the programme for home to write more answers if they can.

The same procedure was continued on the other days also till the completion of the programme. Every day, the investigator had two shifts of 40 minutes each in the two schools as mentioned earlier.

All the days, during the time of training, the students were given full freedom to express themselves in whatever way they like. As the programme maintains the principle of unevaluated practice, students were not evaluated for their responses and they were told that whatever they think and write that is correct. Whenever, students felt any difficulty, investigator was there all the time to remove them. Throughout the training programme, the investigator remained personally present and it was not left to any other person. However, the help of some school teachers were taken to maintain the discipline at the initial stages.

(iv) *Administration of the Post-test (Baquer Mehdi's Verbal and Non-verbal Test of Creative Thinking)*

When the training was over, all the students of treatment and non-treatment groups were again administered the same Baquer Mehdi's Verbal and Non-verbal tests of Creative Thinking to collect the post-test data. It was done again on two consecutive days.

(v) *Administration of CTP Questionnaire*

On the last day, the students of treatment group were given an questionnaire to give their reactions towards the creativity training programme through which they underwent training. It took hardly 30 minutes.

(vi) *Final Setting of the Sample*

At the end of the experiment after the post test, the total sample of 357 students reduced to 285 owing to the drop out of the students at various stages of the training programme. The details of the sample at this stage is given in Table 3.

**Table 3: Showing the Position of the Sample in the Treatment and Non-Treatment Group Sexwise at the End of the Experiment**

| | Treatment Group | Non-Treatment Group | Total |
|---|---|---|---|
| Girls | 64 | 83 | 147 |
| Boys | 60 | 78 | 138 |
| | 124 | 161 | 285 |

To achieve the objectives of the study, the sample was to be stratified according to the students having varying level of intelligence (*i.e.*, high, average and low). This was done at the end of the experiment due to the following reasons:

(i) It was apprehended that there will be quite good number of students who may drop out till the experiment is completed. In that case, the two groups under experiment may not remain equivalent on the bases of their intelligence scores.

(ii) Secondly, it was thought that it would be much easier to match the students of the two groups on their intelligence scores as the non-treatment group will have large number of students as compared to the treatment group.

Keeping these two points in mind, the sample was set at the end of the experiment. For this purpose, each student in the treatment group was matched (approximately) with the students in the non-treatment group on their standard scores of intelligence (Appendix-1) and the students in the non-treatment group who could not be matched were left out. Thus, the sample was further reduced to 248 at this stage as shown in the following table:

Further, as the treatment and non-treatment groups of boys had minimum number of 60 students each, the extra 4 students each from the treatment and non-treatment group of girls (having some intelligence

**Table 4: Showing the Position of the Sample in the Treatment and Non-Treatment Group Sexwise after one to one Matching on the Scores of Intelligence**

| | Treatment Group | Non-Treatment Group | Total |
|---|---|---|---|
| Girls | 64 | 64 | 128 |
| Boys | 60 | 60 | 120 |
| | 124 | 124 | 248 |

score) were discarded randomly so as to have equal number of students in each group. This was done as per suggestion given by Edward (1971)[7]. At this stage, the sample was further reduced to 240 as shown in the following table:

**Table 5: Showing the Position of the Sample in the Treatment and Non-Treatment Group Sexwise after Discarding the Subjects Randomly**

| | Treatment Group | Non-Treatment Group | Total |
|---|---|---|---|
| Girls | 60 | 60 | 120 |
| Boys | 60 | 60 | 120 |
| | 120 | 120 | 240 |

Now the students of both treatment and non-treatment group, boys and girls being taken separately, were arranged in the descending order of their intelligence scores (standard scores) and were then divided in three groups of high, average, and low intelligence level by keeping approximately 68 per cent students in the group of average intelligence level and 16 per cent each in the groups of high and low intelligence level in accordance of normal probability curve. Position of the sample at this stage is shown in the following table:

**Table 6: Showing the Position of the Sample in the Treatment and Non-Treatment Group Sexwise at Different Levels of Intelligence**

| | Treatment Group | Non-Treatment Group | Total |
|---|---|---|---|
| High Level of Intelligence | | | |
| Boys | 10 | 10 | 20 |
| Girls | 10 | 10 | 20 |
| Average Level of Intelligence | | | |
| Boys | 40 | 40 | 80 |
| Girls | 40 | 40 | 80 |
| Low Level of Intelligence | | | |
| Boys | 10 | 10 | 20 |
| Girls | 10 | 10 | 20 |
| Total | 120 | 120 | 240 |

(vii) *Scoring Procedure*

Students on the intelligence tests were scored with the help of the scoring key provided along with the manual of Jalota's General Mental Ability Test. Answer sheets of all the boys and girls students were arranged separately in descending order of their raw scores. These raw score were then converted into standard score (with M = 100, S.D. = 20) for both boys and girls separately. It is on the basis of these scores, the boys and girls students were stratified into three groups of varying intelligence level.

To score the responses of the students on Baquer Mehdi's verbal and non-verbal creativity test, the detailed procedure were followed as given in the manual. Each item was scored separately for fluency, flexibility and originality in the verbal test and for originality and elaboration in the non-verbal test.

In verbal test fluency was scored by counting those responses of the item which were relevant to the activity and have not been repeated. This counted number was then given fluency score for that item. For scoring the flexibility the categories of the various responses on an item were counted as per the scoring guide and this number was then given flexibility score. The scoring of the originality was done on the basis of the uncommonness of the responses as per the direction given in the manual.

For the non-verbal test, the originality was scored again on the basis of uncommonness of the response given for each figural item. For scoring the elaboration, a score of one was given for the primary and minimum responses along with one score each for all the additional new ideas. Here it is to be noted that the titles were not scored for originality and elaboration as they provide data for verbal creativity and not for non-verbal. Data for verbal creativity was taken only from verbal test of creativity. This was done for the sake of convenience.

After scoring for each item of the various activities of both the test the total scores for fluency, flexibility and originality for the verbal test and the total scores for the originality and elaboration were obtained by adding the scores of each item arithmetically as given in the manual.

The composite verbal creativity scores were obtained by adding the scores of total fluency, flexibility and originality arithmetically. Similarly, the composite non-verbal creativity scores were obtained by adding the scores of total originality and elaboration.

Thus, after scoring, the pre-test and post-test raw score data for the various components of verbal and non-verbal creativity as well as for the composite verbal and composite non-verbal creativity were obtained for male and female students (belonging to high, average and low level of intelligence) in the treatment and non-treatment group).

It is to be noted that the investigator has directly added the raw scores of various factors for finding out the composite creativity scores, because a number of investigators have questioned the current practice of finding out the composite scores (Clark and Mirels, 1970[8]; Hocevar and Michael, 1979[9]) on the ground that on conversion to standard scores, flexibility scores of some individuals go higher than their fluency scores which go against the operational definition of creativity as conceptualized by Guilford (1968) and Torrance (1974) maintaining that the flexibility scores can be either equal or less than fluency scores. Moreover, standard scores maintain an individual's position relative to his performance in the group on each of the factor thereby forcing him to have such a score which does not fit into the definition of creativity. Singh (1982)[10] has shown that the raw scores are equally good and reliable as the standard scores. Thus, there seemed no need to put a lot of time and energing in converting the raw scores into standard scores.

**Statistical Analysis Used**

The investigator has used the following statistical techniques to analysis the date which are grouped under the captions as given below:—

(i) F-test to test the significance of the difference between the SD's of the raw score data.

(ii) Analysis of variance (three way: 2×3×2) of difference measures (gain scores) for unequal cells was used to study the significance of difference between treatment and non-treatment groups and as also to find out the interaction among two or more variable under study.

(iii) Hartley's test to test the homogenity of variance within cells.

(iv) t-test to locate the position of significance in case of interaction among two or more independent variables under study.

(v) Percentage of responses on CTP rating scale and CTP questionnaire.

**F-test:** To test the significance among the various SD's of the different factor scores (raw) of verbal and non-verbal creativity, the F-test was applied through the use of variance (Garret, 1971)[11]. The following formula was used to test the significance between two SD's (Garret, 1971)[12].

$$F\text{-ratio} = \frac{\text{Variance (Larger)}}{\text{Variance (Larger)}}$$

Resulting F-value is evaluated in terms of the appropriate df.

Analysis of Variance (Three Way: 2×3×2):

The technique of analysis of variance (three way: 2×3×2) was used to test the significance of difference between treatment and non-treatment groups and as also to find out the interactions among two or more independent variables under study.

As the study involves pre and post test meausres, the analysis of variance of difference measures (Edwad, 1971)[13] was applied where pre and post test score differences (Post-test minus pre-test score) were computed and the gain score of the students was taken as a unit of analysis. This method has also been applied by other researchers (Schuler, 1974[14]; Huber, Treffinger, Tracy and Rand, 1979[15]) in analyzing the data of the same type of experimental study.

Further, as the experimental design involve unequal number of subjects in the various cells, the mean of the gain scores of the students were computed for each cell and this means was taken as a single observation for that cell (Edward, 1971)[16].

The following formula was used to calculate F-ration

$$\text{F - ratio} = \frac{\text{Between Mean Square Variance}}{\text{Error Mean Square}}$$

where—

Error Mean Square = $C_{1.}MS_w$ (Edward, 1971)[17].

where—

$MS_w$ = Within Mean Square,

and, $$C_1 = \frac{1}{k}\sum_{1}^{k}\frac{1}{n_k}$$

where,

k = Total number of cells.

$n_k$ = Number of observations on which cell mean is based.

**Table 7: Showing the Lay-out of the Analysis of Variance (Anova) Table used in the Treatment of Data**

| Source of Variation | df | Sum of Squares (SS) (SS) | Means Square (MS) | F-value |
|---|---|---|---|---|
| A | (a-1) | $SS_A$ | $SS_A/(a-1)$ | $MS_A$/error |
| B | (b-1) | $SS_B$ | $SS_B/(b-1)$ | $MS_B$/error |
| C | (c-1) | $SS_C$ | $SS_C/(c-1)$ | $MS_C$/error |
| A×B | (a-1) (b-1) | $SS_{A\times B}$ | $\frac{SS_{A\times B}}{(a-1)\ (b-1)}$ | $\frac{MS_{A\times B}}{error}$ |
| A×C | (a-1) (c-1) | $SS_{A\times C}$ | $\frac{SS_{A\times C}}{(a-1)\ (c-1)}$ | $\frac{MS_{A\times C}}{error}$ |
| B×C | (a-1) (c-1) | $SS_{B\times C}$ | $\frac{SS_{B\times C}}{(b-1)\ (c-1)}$ | $\frac{MS_{B\times C}}{error}$ |
| A×B×C | (a-1) (b-1) (c-1) | $SS_{A\times B\times C}$ | $\frac{SS_{A\times B\times C}}{(a-1)\ (b-1)\ (c-1)}$ | $\frac{MS_{A\times B\times C}}{error}$ |
| Within | (N-abc) | $SS_W$ | $\frac{SS_W}{(N-abc)}$ | ................ |
| Error | .......... | ............ | $C_{1.}MS_W$ | |

**Table 9: Shows the lay out of analysis of variance (ANOVA) table used in the present study.**

The details of the abbrevetions and formula's used is given below:

A = Treatment conditions.

B = Levels of intelligence.

C = Sex

AxC = Interaction between treatment and the level of intelligence.

AxC = Interaction between treatment and sex.

BxC = Interaction between the level of intelligence and sex.

a = Number of treatment conditions.

b = Number of levels of intelligence.

c = Obvious Number of sex.

SS = Sum of Square.

MS = Mean square.

F = Fisher's Ratio.

$C_1$ = A constant value already described

$MS_w$ = Within mean square (*i.e.* $\frac{SS_W}{N\text{-}abc}$)

$SS_w = \sum_{1}^{k} SS_k$ (Within sum of squares)

where—

$SS_k$ = Sum of square of a cell.

*Hartley's Test*

To test the homogenity within the cells Hartley's test was used with the following formula (Winer, 1962)[19].

$$F_{max} = \frac{\text{Variance (largest)}}{\text{Variance (smallest)}}$$

Resulting F-value is evaluated in terms of the appropriate df.

It is to be noted that before applying the technique of ANOVA to analyse the data, all the assumption underlying the technique of analysis of variance were tested and found satisfactory. The same is described in the chapter-IV while discussing the analysis and interpretation of data.

*t-test:*

Wherever interaction between two or three variables were found significant, 't' test was followed to locate the position of significance. The following formula was used for 't' test.

$$t = \frac{M_1 \quad M_2}{\sqrt{\frac{\sigma_1^2}{N_1} + \frac{\sigma_2^2}{N_2}}}$$

where—

$M_1$-$M_2$ = Difference of the means of the two groups under comparison (say first group and second group)

$\sigma_1$ = Standard deviation of the first group.

$\sigma_2$ = Standard deviation of the second group.

$N_1$ = Number of subjects in the first group.

$N_2$ = Number of subjects in the second group.

*Percentage:*

With regard to the data obtained on the CTP rating scale and CTP questionnaire, percentage of the various responses for each item was calculated.

Foot Notes:

1. Lokesh Kaul. *Methodology of Educational Research.* Vikas Publishing House, New Delhi, 1984, p. 441.
2. Allen L. Edwards. *Experimental Design in Psychological Research.* Indian Edition. Amerind Publishing Co. Pvt. Ltd., New Delhi, 1971, pp. 200-223.
3. F.N. Kerlinger. *Foundation of Behavioural Research.* Second Edition, First Indian Reprint. Surjeet Publications, New Delhi, 1978, p. 351.
4. Jalota. *The Group Test of General Mental Ability:* Psycho-Centre, 27-Green Park, New Delhi.
5. Baquer Mehdi. *Verbal Test of Creative Thinking,* Published by Mrs. Qamar Fatima, Aligarh, 1873.
6. Baquer Mehdi. *Non-verbal Test of Creative Thinking.* Published by Mrs. Qamar Fatima, Aligarh, 1973.
7. Allen L. Edwards. *Experimental Design in Psychological Research.* Indian Edition. Amerind Publishing Co. Pvt. Ltd., New Delhi, 1971, pp. 263-264.
8. P. Clark and H. Mirels. Fluency as a Pervasive element in measurement of creativity. *Journal of Educational Measurement.* 7, 83-86.
9. D. Hocevar, and W.B. Michael. The effects of scoring formula on the discriminant validity of tests of creative thinking. *Educational and* Psychological Measurement, 39, 917-921.
10. K. Singh. Problems in Measurement of creative thinking. *ISPI Journal of Research in Educational & Psychological Measurement.* Vol. VI, No. 2, July 1982, ISPT, pp. 22-25.
11. Henery, E. Garret. *Statistics in Psychology and Education,* Vakil, Feffer and Simons, 1971, p. 303.
12. *Ibid.*, p. 303.

13. Allen L. Edward. *Experimental Design in Psychology and Research,* Amerind Publishing Co. Pvt. Ltd., New Delhi, pp. 343-344.
14. G. Schuler. *The effectiveness of the productive thinking programme,* Ithaca, N.Y.: Ithaca College, 1974.
15. J. Huber, D. Treffinger, D. Tracy, and D. Rand. Self-Instructional use of programmed creativity training materials with gifted and regular students. *Journal of Educational Psychology,* 1979, Vol. 71, No. 3, pp. 303-309.
16. Allen L. Edward. *Experimental Design in Psychological Research,* Amerind Publishing Co. Pvt. Ltd., New Delhi, 1977, p. 26.
17. *Ibid,* p. 265.
18. Winer, B.J. *Statistical Principles in Experimental* Design, McGraw Hill, Kogakusha, Ltd., Tokyo, 1962, p. 206.

# five

## ANALYSIS AND INTERPRETATION

The design of this investigation was presented in third Chapter and the investigator had framed certain hypotheses to be tested with the help of the data collected during the investigation. The present chapter presents the analysis and interpretation of the data.

Before we do so, it would be worth-while to recall the outline of the research design, variables involved and statistical technique used to analyze the data. The present study involved a three dimensional (2×3×2) factorial design with three independent variables (namely, treatment, intelligence level and sex) and seven dependent variables (*viz.*, verbal fluency, verbal flexibility, verbal originality, composite verbal creativity, non-verbal originality, non-verbal elaboration and composite non-verbal creativity).

Using this three dimensional factorial design, three ways analysis of variance of difference measures was applied to analyze the data for each dependent variable separately. As already described, for this purpose the unit of analysis was taken as the gain score of the students on the dependent variable under study. Further mean of the gain scores has been taken as a single observation for each cell because of the unequal number of subjects in the various cells of the design.

Further, before proceeding with the computation of data through the analysis of variance, the following basic assumptions underlying the technique of analysis of variance were tested (Guilford, 1956)[1].

(i) **Assumption of normality:** In the light of the findings of Norton (Guilford, 1956)[2] the assumption of normality may not be considered important for the data of the experiment.

(ii) **Assumption of randomness:** The requirement of randomness has been amply fulfilled in this experiment as the subjects were randomly assigned to the treatment and non-treatment group.

(iii) **Assumption of homogenity of variance:** One of the basic assumption underlying the technique of ANOVA is that the variance within cells should be homogeneous. In the light of the findings of Box (Winer, 1962)[3], moderate departures from this assumption do not, however, seriously effect the sampling distribution of the resulting F-statistic because F-test is quite robust with respect to the departures from homogenity of variance. Guilford (1956)[4] has also mentioned that only marked differences in variance are serious and a rough test as suggested by Hartley can be applied to check the homogenity of variance within groups. Guilford (1956)[5] further mentions that even if some where significant differences are found within some groups, one may proceed with the analysis of variance.

Therefore, Hartley's test which is relatively simple and ensures only rough check was applied to test the homogenity of the variance within groups. It was found in almost all the ANOVA's data that the within group variance does not differe much and thus can be said approximately equal.

**(iv) Assumption of additivity:** The assumption of additivity of variances was held satisfied because the variances of the scores of each factor of creativity (both verbal and non-verbal) can be added up separately.

After finding out that the assumption underlying the analysis of variance are almost satisfied, the investigator applied the technique of ANOVA to analyse the data. Separate analysis was done for each of the dependent variable under study.

Analysis and interpretation of data is now discussed in the following two sections:

(i) Effectiveness of Creativity Training Programme.

(ii) Reactions of Students towards creativity Training Programme.

**Effectiveness of Creativity Programme**

The analysis and interpretation of data with regards to the effectiveness of CTP is discussed under the seven heads as given below:—

1. Creativity of Training Programme (CTP) and Verbal Fluency.
   1. Main effect of CTP on the development of verbal fluency.
   2. Interaction effect of CTP with intelligence on the development of verbal fluency.
   3. Interaction effect of CTP with sex on the development of verbal fluency.
   4. Interaction effect of CTP with intelligence and sex (taken together) on the development of verbal fluency.
2. Creativity Training Programme (CTP) and Verbal Flexibiligy.
   1. Main effect of CTP on the development of verbal flexibility.
   2. Interaction effect of CTP with intelligence on the development of verbal flexibility.
   3. Interaction effect of CTP with sex on the development of verbal flexibility.
   4. Interaction effect of CTP with intelligence and sex (taken together) on the development of verbal flexibility.

3. Creativity Training Programme (CTP) and verbal originality.
   1. Main effect of CTP on the development of verbal originality.
   2. Interaction effect of CTP with intelligence on the development of verbal originality.
   3. Interaction effect of CTP with sex on the development of verbal originality.
   4. Interaction effect of CTP with intelligence and sex (taken together) on the development of verbal originality.
4. Creativity Training Programme (CTP) and Composite Verbal Creativity.
   1 Main effect of CTP on the development of composite verbal creativity.
   2. Interaction effect of CTP with intelligence on the development of composite verbal creativity.
   3. Interaction effect of CTP with sex on the development of composite verbal creativity.
   4. Interaction effect of CTP with intelligence and sex (taken together) on the development of composite verbal creativity.
5. Creativity Training Programme (CTP) and Non-Verbal Originality.
   1. Main effect of CTP on the development of non-verbal originality.
   2. Interaction effect of CTP with intelligence on the development of non-verbal originality.

3. Interaction effect of CTP with sex on the development of non-verbal originality.
4. Interaction effect of CTP with intelligence and sex (taken together) on the development of non-verbal originality.

6. Creativity Training Programme (CTP) and non-verbal Elaboration.
   1. Main effect of CTP on the development of non-verbal elaboration.
   2. Interaction effect of CTP with intelligence on the development of non-verbal elaboration.
   3. Interaction effect of CTP with sex on the development of non-verbal elaboration.
   4. Interaction effect of CTP with intelligence and sex (taken together) on the development of non-verbal elaboration.
7. Creativity Training Programme (CTP) and Composite Non-verbal Creativity.
   1. Main effect of CTP on the development of composite non-verbal creativity.
   2. Interaction effect of CTP with intelligence on the development of composite non-verbal creativity.
   3. Interaction effect of CTP with sex on the development of composite non-verbal creativity.
   4. Interaction effect of CTP with intelligence and sex (taken together) on the development of composite non-verbal creativity.

1. ***Creativity Training Programme (CTP) and Verbal Fluency***

Table 2 shows the summary of the analysis of variance (2 × 3 × 2) for verbal fluency.

Table 1: Showing the summary of the analysis of variance (2 × 3 × 2) for verbal fluency

| Source of Variation | Sum of Squares | df | Mean Square | F-ratio |
|---|---|---|---|---|
| A | 675.60 | 1 | 675.60 | 127.23* |
| B | 63.70 | 2 | 31.85 | 6.25* |
| C | 0.70 | 1 | 0.70 | 0.13 |
| A×B | 10.61 | 2 | 5.30 | 1.04 |
| A×C | 8.66 | 1 | 8.66 | 1.70 |
| B×C | 48.45 | 2 | 24.22 | 4.75* |
| A×B×C | 7.96 | 2 | 3.98 | 0.78 |
| Error | ..... | 228 | 5.31 | ..... |

* Significant at .01 level

Index :

A : Treatment conditions (CTP vs No Training)
B : Level of Intelligence (High vs Average vs Low)
C : Sex (Male vs Female)

It is to be noted from the Table 2 that the total variance has been duly partitioned so as to denote the variance due to main effects namely, treatment conditions (A), intelligence level (B), and sex (C). Besides this, variance contributed by any two effects at a time (first order interaction) *viz.*, A×B, B×C and A×C and Variance due to all the three main effects taken together (second order interaction) *viz.*, A×B×C have also been isolated.

It is revealed from the table that for verbal fluency, out of the three main effects, two are significant *viz.*, treatment (F = 127.23, df = 1/228, P. < .01) and intelligence level (F = 6.25, df = 2/228, p. < .01) former being highly significant. With regard to the first order interactions, only one due to intelligence and sex (B×C) came out to be significant (F = 4.75, df = 2/228, P < .01) while the interaction of treatment with intelligence (A×B) and with sex (A×C) were not found to be significant. The second order interaction due to the combined effect of treatment with intelligence and sex (A×B×C) has also come insignificant.

Before these results are further discussed it is to be noted that since the hypotheses for the present study are concerned for the treatment effects only, the other effects which do not involve treatment are not the part of discussion of the present study.

*Main effect of CTP on the development of Verbal Fluency*

With regard to the significance of F-ratio for the main effect of treatment for verbal fluency as described above, the Table 2 further shows the difference between the mean gain scores of the treatment and non-treatment group.

**Table 2: Showing the Difference between the mean gain scores of the treatment and non-treatment group for verbal Fluency**

| | Mean Gain Score | Difference of Mean |
|---|---|---|
| Treatment Group | 20.27 | 15.89 |
| Non-Treatment Group | 4.38 | |

From Table-10, it is evident that the difference in the mean gain scores is in the favour of treatment group. Thus, the greater mean gain value on the verbal fluency for the treatment group as compared to the non-treatment group reveals that the students who underwent training through CTP improved their verbal fluency against their counterparts in the non-treatment group who had their regular class room teaching instead of getting training through CTP. This suggests that creativity training programme was effective as far as the development of verbal fluency is concerned.

*Interaction effect of CTP with intelligence on the development of verbal fluency*

Table 1 shows that the interaction between CTP and intelligence is insignificant as the F-ratio (*i.e.*, 1.04) does not reach to the significant value even at .05 level (F=3.04 with df = 2/228). It indicates that the level of intelligence of the students does not influence the effect of creativity training programme in developing verbal fluency. This further reveals that the programme is equally effective at all the level of intelligence.

*Interaction effect of CTP with sex on the development of verbal fluency*

The interaction between CTP and sex has also not come significant as the F-value of 1.70 as shown in the Table 1 was found below than the required value of 3.89 to gain significance at .05 level with df = 1/228. It suggests that sex also does not influence the effect of CTP in developing verbal fluency.

*Interaction effect of CTP with intelligence and sex (taken together) on the development of verbal fluency*

With regard to the interaction effect of CTP with intelligence and sex (both taken together) on the development of verbal fluency, the F-value (0.78) as shown in Table 1 was too not found significant. It means that the students of a particular sex having a particular level of intelligence does not influence the effect of CTP on the development of verbal fluency. In other words, it can be said that the programme is equally effective for both male and female students irrespective of their level of intelligence with regard to the development of verbal fluency.

**Creativity Training Programme (CTP) and Verbal Flexibility**

Table 3 shows the summary of the analysis of variance (2×3×2) for verbal flexibility.

Table 3 reveals that for verbal flexibility only treatment effect is significant (F = 31.13, df = 1/228, P < .01). As for as the first order interaction is concerned, none has been found to gain significance even at .05 level. The same is the case of second order interaction (A×B×C) which has not reached to the significance level even at .05 level.

**Table 3: Showing the summary of analysis of variance (2 × 3 × 2) for verbal flexibility**

| Source of Variation | Sum of Squares | df | Mean Square | F-ratio |
|---|---|---|---|---|
| A | 39.85 | 1 | 39.85 | 31.13* |
| B | 4.51 | 2 | 2.25 | 1.75 |
| C | 0.09 | 1 | 0.09 | 0.07 |
| A×B | 2.63 | 2 | 1.31 | 1.02 |
| A×C | 0.30 | 1 | 0.30 | 0.23 |
| B×C | 1.49 | 2 | 0.74 | 0.57 |
| A×B×C | 3.77 | 2 | 1.88 | 1.46 |
| Error | -- | 228 | 1.28 | -- |

* Significant at .01 level

Index:

A : Treatment conditions (CTP vs No Training)

B : Level of Intelligence (High vs Average vs Low)

C : Sex (Male vs Female)

### *Main effect of CTP on the development of Verbal Flexibility*

F-ratio has already been found significant for the main effect of treatment in the case of verbal flexibility. The Table 4 further shows the difference between the mean gain scores of the treatment and non-treatment group.

It is evident from Table 4 that difference in the mean gain scores is in the favour of treatment group. It indicates that the students who underwent the training through CTP significantly improved their verbal flexibility when they are compared with the students of non-treatment group who did not had such training. This implies that the creativity training programme is significantly effective in developing verbal flexibility of the students in the treatment group.

**Table 4: Showing the difference between the mean gain scores of the treatment and non-treatment groups for verbal flexibility**

| | Mean Gain Scores | Difference |
|---|---|---|
| Treatment Group | 7.89 | |
| Non-Treatment Group | 3.65 | 4.24 |

### *Interaction effect of CTP with Intelligence on the development of verbal flexibility*

With regard to the interaction of CTP with intelligence, Table 3 shows that the F-ratio (*i.e.*, 1.02) has not come significant even at .05 level (F = 3.04 with df = 2.228). It reveals that the level of intelligence of the students does not influence the development of verbal flexibility when the students undergo training through creativity training programme, which further indicates that the programme is equally effective at all the level of intelligence.

### *Interaction effect of CTP with sex on the development of verbal flexibility*

Table 3 reveals that the interaction between CTP and sex too is insignificant as the F-ratio (*i.e.*, 0.23) does not gain the significant value even at .05 level (F = 3.89 with df = 1/228). It indicates that there is no influence of sex on the effect of CTP in developing verbal flexibility. In other words, we can say that both male and female got equally benefited through CTP in developing their verbal flexibility.

2.4. Interaction effect of CTP with intelligence and sex (taken together) on the development of verbal flexibility:

As for as the interaction of CTP with intelligence and sex (both taken together) on the development of verbal flexibility is concerned, the F-value (*i.e.*, 1.46) as shown in Table 3 has also not been found significant. It suggests that the students of a particular sex having a particular level of intelligence does not influence the effect of CTP on the development of verbal flexibility. In other words, it can be said that the programme is equally effective with regard to the development of verbal flexibility in both male and female irrespective of their intelligence level.

**Creativity Training Programme (CTP) and Verbal Originality**

Table 5 shows the summary of the analysis of variance (2×3×2) for verbal originality.

From the Table 5, it is revealed that for verbal originality, out of the three main effects, two are significant *viz.*, treatment (F = 51.94, df = 1/228, P < .01) and intelligence level (F = 17.27, df = 2/228, P < .01). But the main effect due to the intelligence is not the part of our discussion as the hypotheses for the present study are concerned for the effects where the treatment is involved.

With regard to the first order interactions only

one due to the treatment and sex (A×B) has come out to be significant (F = 4.59, df = 2/228, P < .05) which will be discussed later in detail. The other second order interactions of treatment with sex (A×C) and of intelligence with sex (B×C) were found to be insignificant. As for as the second order interaction of treatment with intelligence and sex (A×B×C) is concerned, the table-13, reveals that it is also not significant. The interaction between intelligence and sex is not discussed as already. stated.

**Table 5: Showing the summary of analysis of variance (2×3×2) for verbal originality**

| Source of Variation | Sum of Squares | df | Mean Square | F-ratio |
|---|---|---|---|---|
| A | 96.61 | 1 | 96.61 | 51.94* |
| B | 64.27 | 2 | 32.13 | 17.27* |
| C | 0.11 | 1 | 0.11 | 0.06 |
| A×B | 17.09 | 2 | 8.54 | 4.59* |
| A×C | 5.67 | 1 | 5.67 | 3.05 |
| B×C | 14.85 | 2 | 7.42 | 3.99** |
| A×B×C | 4.33 | 2 | 2.16 | 1.16 |
| Error | --- | 228 | 1.86 | --- |

* Significant at .01 level; ** Significant at .05 level

Index : A : Treatment conditions (CTP vx No Training).
B : Level of Intelligence (High vs Average vs Low).
C : Sex (Male vs Female)

### *Main effect of CTP on the development of Verbal Originality*

As already described above, the F-ratio for the main effect of treatment for verbal originality is significant at .01 level. Table 6 further shows the difference between the mean gain scores of the treatment and non-treatment group.

Table 6 shows that the difference in the mean gain scores is in the favour of the treatment group. This greater mean value on the verbal originality for the treatment group reveals that the students who underwent training through CTP improved their verbal originality against their counter parts in the non-treatment group who had their regular class room teaching instead of getting training through CTP. This indicates that the creativity training programme was effective in developing verbal originality among the students in the treatment group.

**Table 6: Showing the Difference Between the mean gain scores of the treatment and non-treatment groups for verbal originality**

| | Mean Gain Score | Difference of Means |
|---|---|---|
| Treatment Group | 8.35 | 4/82 |
| Non-Treatment Group | 3.53 | |

***Interaction effect of CTP with intelligence on the development of verbal originality***

Unlike verbal fluency and verbal flexibility, the interaction effect of CTP with intelligence has been found significant at .05 level (F = 4.59, df = 2/228, P < .05) for verbal originality. It indicates that the level of intelligence does influence the effect of CTP in developing verbal originality of the students. To find out further that at what level of intelligence the CTP is more effective, the 't' test is followed the result of which are shown in Table 7.

**Table 7: Showing the t-values for the significance of difference between the mean gain scores for the students belonging to high, average and low leave of intelligence in the treatment and non-treatment group for verbal originality**

| | | N | M | S.D. | Difference of means | t-value |
|---|---|---|---|---|---|---|
| | Treatment Group $A_1$ | 10 | 14.35 | 7.3 | | |
| High level of Intelligence $B_1$ | | | | | 9.05 | 3.40* |
| | Non-Treatment Group $A_2$ | 10 | 5.3 | 4.20 | | |
| | Treatment Group $A_1$ | 40 | 7.29 | 5.8 | | |
| Average Level of Intelligence $B_2$ | | | | | 3.97 | 3.64* |
| | Non-Treatment Group $A_2$ | 40 | 3.72 | 3.32 | | |
| | Treatment Group $A_1$ | 10 | 6.6 | 5.0 | | |
| Low Level of Intelligence $B_3$ | | | | | 4.00 | 2.08 |
| | Non-Treatment Goup $A_2$ | 10 | 2.6 | 3.44 | | |

* Significant at .01 level.

Table 7 shows the significant t-values for the students of high (t=3.40, df = 18) and average (t=3.64, df = 78) intelligence level in the favour of treatment group while the same has not been found significant for the students in the low group of intelligence level. It means that the level of intelligence influences the effect of CTP in developing verbal originality in students.

The above Table 7 shows the significant t-values at .01 level for the students of high (t = 3.40, df = 18) and average (t = 3.64, df = 78) intelligence level in the favour of treatment group as the mean gain score of the treatment group is greater than the mean gain score of the non-treatment group in both the cases. Though the T-value has not come significant for the students in the low group of intelligence but its high t-value (*i.e.*, 2.08) which is quite near at .05 level indicates that the students of low intelligence level are also able to get at least some benefit out of the programme in developing their verbal originality.

It indicates that the creativity training programme is more effective for the students of high and average level of intelligence as compared to the students of low level of intelligence in developing verbal originality.

Further, as the difference in the mean gain scores (*i.e.*, 9.05) between the treatment and non-treatment group of high intelligence level is more than the mean gain scores (*i.e.*, 3.97) between the treatment and non-treatment group of average intelligence level, it seems that the creativity training programme is more effective for the students of high level of intelligence as compared to the students of average level of intelligence. In other words the students having high intelligence seem to benefit more from CTP than the students of average intelligence, who in turn, benefit more than the students of low intelligence in developing their verbal originality.

***Interaction effect of CTP with sex on the development of Verbal Originality***

Table 5 reveals that though the interaction between CTP and sex is not significant as the F-ratio (*i.e.*, 3.05) was found to be below than the required value of 3.89 to gain significance at .05 level with df = 1/228, but the high value of F-ratio indicates that the CTP may be more effective for a particular sex. The Table 8 will further clarify the position.

**Table 8: Showing the difference between the mean gain scores of the treatment and Non-Treatment group of male and female students for verbal originality**

| Sex | Group | Mean Gain Scores | Difference of Means |
|---|---|---|---|
| Male | Treatment | 30.02 | 21.15 |
| | Non-Treatment | 8.87 | |
| Female | Treatment | 26.47 | 12.90 |
| | Non-Treatment | 13.57 | |

Table 8 shows that the difference between the mean gain scores of the treatment and non-treatment group is more in favour of male children. Thus, it appears that the male children are likely to benefit more from CTP as against female children in developing their verbal originality.

***Interaction effect of CTP with Intelligence and Sex (Taken together) on the development of verbal originality***

Though the interaction between CTP and intelligence has come out significant along with some partial interaction between CTP and sex also, the value of F-ratio (*i.e.*, 1.16) for the combined interaction among CTP, intelligence and sex has not been found significant statistically even at .05 level of significance. It appears that though the intelligence and sex may have their independent influence on the effect of CTP in developing verbal originality, but when these two variable combine together (*i.e.*, intelligence and sex), their influence on the effect of CTP remains no longer. It implies that in developing verbal originality also, the programme is equally effective for both male and female students irrespective of their level of intelligence.

**Creativity Training Programme (CTP) and Composite Verbal Creativity**

Table 9 shows the summary of the analysis of

variance (2×3×2) for composite verbal creativity.

It is revealed from the Table 9 that treatment effect is highly significant (F = 138.12, df = 1/228, P, .01). With regard to the first order interactions, only one due to intelligence and sex (B×C) was found to be significant (F = 4.02, df = 2/228, P < .01), while the interaction of the treatment with intelligence (A×B) and sex (A×C) are insignificant. The second order interaction due to the combined effect of treatment with intelligence and sex (A×B×C) has also not been found significant. Though, there is a significant interaction between intelligence and sex (B×C) as already stated, but it will not be discussed owing to the reasons mentioned earlier.

**Table 9: Showing the summary of analysis of variance (2×3×2) for composite verbal creativity**

| Square of variation | Sum of Squares | df | Mean Square | F-ratio |
|---|---|---|---|---|
| A | 1841.22 | 1 | 1841.22 | 138.12* |
| B | 290.96 | 2 | 145.48 | 10.91 |
| C | 0.68 | 1 | 0.68 | 0.05 |
| A×B | 20.24 | 2 | 10.12 | 0.76 |
| A×C | 37.12 | 1 | 37.12 | 2.78 |
| B×C | 107.22 | 2 | 53.61 | 4.02** |
| A×B×C | 33.48 | 2 | 16.74 | 1.25 |
| Error | --- | 228 | 13.33 | ---- |

* Significant at .01 level.

** Significant at .05 level.

Index :

A : Treatment condition (CTP vs No-Training)

B : Level of Intelligence (High vs Average vs Low)

C : Sex (Male vs Female)

*Main effect of CTP on the development of composite Verbal Originality*

It has already been found that the F-ratio is highly significant for the main effect of treatment with regard to the composite verbal originality. Table 10 further shows the difference between the mean gain scores of the treatment and non-treatment group.

**Table 10: Showing the difference between the mean gain scores of the treatment and non-treatment groups for composite verbal creativity**

| | Mean Gain Scores | Difference of Means |
|---|---|---|
| Treatment Group | 36.65 | 25.17 |
| Non-Treatment Group | 11.48 | |

It is evident from the Table 10 that the mean gain score of treatment group is greater than the non-treatment group by a difference of 25.17 points. This high difference in the mean gain scores of the treatment group against the non-treatment group clearly indicates that the students who underwent training through CTP improved quite high as compared to the non-treatment group who did not had such training and were studying in regular class room as usual. This implies that the creativity training programme is highly effective in developing composite verbal creativity of the students in the treatment group.

*Internation of CTP with intelligence on the development of Composite Verbal Creativity*

With regard to the interaction of CTP with intelligence, Table 9 shows that the value of F-ratio (*i.e.*, 0.76) is quite low to reach at significance level. It indicates that the level of intelligence of the students does not influence the development of composite verbal creativity when the students undergo training through CTP. It appears that the programme is equally effective at all the level of intelligence as far as the development of composite verbal creativity is concerned.

***Interaction of CTP with sex on the development of composite verbal creativity***

As revealed from the Table 9, though the interaction between CTP and sex is not significant ($F = 2.78$, $df = 1/228$, $p > .05$) for composite verbal creativity, but the high F-value indicates that the CTP may be

**Table 11: Showing the difference between the mean gain scores of the treatment and Non-treatment groups of male and female students for composites verbal creativity**

| Sex | Group | Mean Gain Scores | Difference of Means |
|---|---|---|---|
| Male | Treatment | 115.52 | 85.12 |
| | Non-Treatment | 30.40 | |
| Female | Treatment | 106.12 | 53.45 |
| | Non-Treatment | 42.67 | |

little more effective for a particular sex. It may be more clarified by studying the difference between the mean gain scores of the treatment and non-treatment groups of male and female students. The same is shown in Table 11.

From Table 11, it appears that the male children are likely to benefit more from CTP as against female children in developing their composite verbal creativity, as the difference between the mean gain scores of the treatment and non-treatment group is more in favour of the male students.

***Interaction effect of CTP with intelligence and sex (taken together) on the development of composite verbal creativity***

As already discussed, no interaction is revealed among CTP, intelligence and sex with regard to the verbal fluency, flexibility and originality. The same is the case with regard to the composite verbal creativity as F-value (*i.e.*, 1.25) has not come out significant even at .05 level (Table 9). It appears that the effect of CTP on the development of composite verbal originality also is not being influenced by the students of a particular sex having a particular intelligence level. In other words, the CTP is equally effective for both male and female students irrespective of their level of intelligence as far as the development of composite verbal creativity is concerned.

**Creativity Training Programme (CTP) and Non-Verbal Originality**

Table 12 shows the summary of the analysis of variance (2×3×2) for non-verbal originality.

It is revealed from the Table 12 that the main

effect only due to treatment is significant (F=54.61, df = 1.228, P < .01). Other two main effects due to intelligence and sex were found insignificant. Besides, none of the first order interaction (*i.e.*, AxB, AxC, and AxB) and second order interaction (*i.e.*, (AxBxC) have been found significant even at .05 level.

**Table 12: Showing the summary of analysis of variance (2x3x2) for non-verbal originality**

| Source of variation | Sum of squares | df | Mean square | F-ration |
|---|---|---|---|---|
| A | 60.07 | 1 | 60.07 | 54.61* |
| B | 17.60 | 2 | 8.8 | 8.00 |
| C | 0.22 | 1 | 0.22 | 0.20 |
| AxB | 1.72 | 2 | 0.86 | 0.78 |
| AxC | 0.04 | 1 | 0.04 | 0.036 |
| BxC | 0.75 | 2 | 0.37 | 0.336 |
| AxBxC | 1.53 | 2 | 0.76 | 0.69 |
| Error | --- | 228 | 1.10 | --- |

* Significant at .01 level

Index:

A : Treatment conditions (CTP vs No Training)

B : Level of intelligence (High vs Average vs Low)

C : Sex (Male vs Female)

### *Main Effect of CTP on the Development of non-verbal originality*

It has already been found that the F-ratio is highly significant for the main effect of treatment with regard to the development of non-verbal originality. In this connection, Table 13 shows the difference between the mean gain scroes of the treatment and non-treatment groups which will further clarify the effectiveness of CTP.

Table 13: Showing the Difference Between the mean Gain Scores of the Treatment and Non-Treatment Groups for Non-Verbal Originality

| | Mean Gain Scores | Difference of Means |
|---|---|---|
| Treatment Group | 8.20 | 4.35 |
| Non-Treatment Group | 3.85 | |

It is clear from the Table 13 that the mean gain score of treatment group is greater than the non-treatment group by a difference of 4.35 points. It indicates that the students who underwent the training through CTP improved their non-verbal originality as against the students of non-treatment group who did not such training and were studying in their regular class room as usual. This indicates that the creativity training programme is significantly effective in developing non-verbal originality of the students in the treatment group.

*Interaction effect of CTP with intelligence on the development of non-verbal originality*

As far as the interaction of CTP with intelligence is concerned, Table 12 reveals that the F-ratio (*i.e.*, 0.78) is very low, thus making it quite insignificant. It indicates that the level of intelligence does not influence on the effect of creativity training programme in developing non-verbal originality in students. This further suggests that the creativity training programme is equally effective at all levels of intelligence.

*Interaction effect of CTP with sex on the development of non-verbal originality*

The interaction between CTP and sex has also not been found significant for non-verbal originality as the F-value (*i.e.*, 0.036) is quite low. It indicates that the sex also does not interfere on the effect of CTP in developing non-verbal originality in students. In other words, it can be said that both male and female students got equally benefited through CTP in developing their non-verbal originality. However, if we compare it with verbal originality the case is not so where male students had better gains as against to the female students.

*Interaction effect of CTP with intelligence and sex (taken together) on the development of non-verbal originality*

With regard to the interaction effect of CTP with intelligence and sex on the development of non-verbal originality, the F-ratio (*i.e.*, 0.69) as shown in Table 12 was too not found significant. It means that the students of a particular sex having a particular level of inelligence does not influence the effect of CTP in developing non-verbal originality of the students. In other words, it can be said that both male and female students, irrespective of their intelligence level, got equally benefited in developing their non-verbal originality.

**Creativity Training Programme (CTP) and Non-Verbal Elaboration**

Table 14 shows the summary of the analysis of variance (2×3×2) for non-verbal elaboration.

It is revealed from the Table 14 that the main effect due to treatment is highly significant (F = 43.11, df = 1/228, P < .01) for non-verbal elaboration. With regard to the first order interactions (*viz.*, A×B, A×C and B×C) and second order interaction (*viz.*, A×B×C) none has been found significant.

*Main effect of CTP on the development of non-verbal elaboration*

F-ratio has already been found significant for the main effect of treatment in the case of non-verbal elaboration as described above. The Table-23 further shows the difference between the mean gain scores of the treatment and non-treatment group with regard to the non-verbal elaboration.

From Table 15, it is evident that the difference in the mean gain scores is in the favour of treatment group. It indicates that the students who underwent training through CTP improved their non-verbal elaboration as against the students who did not had such training. This implies that the creativity training programme is significantly effective in developing the non-verbal elaboration of the students in the treatment group.

Table 14: Showing the summary of analysis of variance (2×3×2) for non-verbal elaboration

| Source of variation | Sum of squares | df | Mean square | F-ration |
|---|---|---|---|---|
| A | 69.84 | 1 | 69.84 | 43.11* |
| B | 8.00 | 2 | 4.00 | 2.47 |
| C | 0.82 | 1 | 0.82 | 0.51 |
| AxB | 0.79 | 2 | 0.39 | 0.24 |
| AxC | 0.65 | 1 | 0.65 | 0.40 |
| BxC | 1.78 | 2 | 0.89 | 0.55 |
| AxBxC | 0.39 | 2 | 0.19 | 0.12 |
| Error | --- | 228 | 1.62 | --- |

* Significant at .01 level

Index:

A : Treatment conditions (CTP vs No Training)

B : Level of intelligence (High vs Average vs Low)

C : Sex (Male vs Female)

Table 15: Showing the Difference Between the Mean Gain Scores of the Treatment and Non-Treatment Groups for Non-Verbal Elaboration

| | Mean Gain Score | Difference of Means |
|---|---|---|
| Treatment Group | 8.35 | 4.55 |
| Non-Treatment Group | 3.80 | |

***Interaction effect of CTP with intelligence on the development of non-verbal elaboration***

With regard to the interaction of CTP with intelligence, Table 14 shows that the F-ratio (*i.e.*, 0.24) is quite low to gain significance even at .05 level. It indicates that the level of intelligence does not influence the effect of creativity training programme in developing non-verbal elaboration, which further reveals that the programme is equally effective at all the level of intelligence.

*Interaction effect of CTP with sex on the development of non-verbal elaboration*

Table 14 reveals that the interaction between CTP and sex has also not come significant as the F-ratio (*i.e.*, 0.40) in this case too is very low so as to be significant. It indicates that the sex also does not influence the effect of CTP in developing non-verbal elaboration. It means that both boys and girls got equally benefited through CTP as far as the development of non-verbal elaboration is concerned.

*Interaction effect of CTP with intelligence and sex (taken together on the development of non-verbal elaboration*

With regard to the interaction of CTP with intelligence and sex (both taken together) on the development of non-verbal elaboration, the F-value (*i.e.*, 0.12) as shown in the Table-22 is too quite low, thereby indicating the insignificance of the interaction. It indicates that the students of a particular sex having a particular level of intelligence does not influence the effect of CTP on the development of non-verbal elaboration. In other words, it can be said that the programme is equally effective in developing non-verbal elaboration of both male and female students irrespective of their intelligence level.

Creativity Training Programme (CTP) and Compist Non-Verbal Creativity

Table 16 shows the summary of the analysis of

variance (2×3×2) for composite non-verbal creativity.

**Table 16: Showing the summary of analysis of variance (2×3×2) for composite non-verbal creativity**

| Source of variation | Sum of squares | df | Mean square | F-ratio |
|---|---|---|---|---|
| A | 260.86 | 1 | 260.86 | 85.52* |
| B | 46.32 | 2 | 23.16 | 7.59 |
| C | 2.03 | 1 | 2.03 | 0.66 |
| A×B | 5.32 | 2 | 2.66 | 0.87 |
| A×C | 0.92 | 1 | 0.92 | 0.30 |
| B×C | 4.57 | 2 | 2.28 | 0.74 |
| A×B×C | 0.53 | 2 | 0.26 | 0.08 |
| Error | --- | 228 | 3.05 | --- |

* Significant at .01 level

Index:

A : Treatment conditions (CTP vs No Training)

B : Level of intelligence (High vs Average vs Low)

C : Sex (Male vs Female)

From Table 16, it is revealed that the main effect of treatment is highly significant (F = 85.52, df = 1/228, $P < .01$). With regard to the first order interaction (*viz.*, A×B, A×C, and B×C) and second order interaction (*viz.*, A×B×C), none has been found significant.

*Main effect of CTP on the development of composite non-verbal creativity*

As already described above, the F-ratio for main effect of treatment for composite non-verbal creativity is significant at .01 level. Table 17 further shows the difference between the mean gain scores of the treatment and non-treatment.

Table 17: Showing the Difference between the mean gain scores of the treatment and non-treatment groups for composite non-verbal creativity

| | Mean Gain Scores | Difference of Means |
|---|---|---|
| Treatment Group | 16.55 | 8.95 |
| Non-Treatment Group | 7.60 | |

Table 17 reveals that the difference in the mean gain scores is in the favour of treatment group. Thus, the greater mean gain value on the composite non-verbal creativity for the treatment group as compared to the non-treatment group indicates that the students who underwent training through CTP improved their composite non-verbal creativity as against their counterparts in the non-treatment group who had their regular class room teaching instead of getting training through CTP. This implies that the creativity training programme was highly effective in developing composite non-verbal creativity of the students in the treatment group.

*Interaction effect of CTP with intelligence on the development of composite non-verbal creativity*

Table 16 further reveals that the interaction between CTP and intelligence is insignificant for composite non-verbal creativity as the F-ratio (*i.e.*, 0.87) is quite low. It indicates the level of intelligence of the students does not influence the effect of creativity training programme in developing composite non-verbal creativity also. This further reveals that the programme is equally effective at all the level of intelligence as far as the development of composite non-verbal creativity is concerned.

*Interaction effect of CTP with sex on the development of composite non-verbal creativity*

With regard to the interaction of CTP with sex, Table 16 reveals that it too is not significant as the value of F-ratio (*i.e.*, 0.30) is far below to gain significance even at .05 level (F = 3.89, df = 1/228). It indicates that like intelligence, sex also does not influence the effect of CTP in developing composite non-verbal creativity of the students in the treatment group. In other words, it can be said that the programme is equally effective for both male and female as far as the development of composite non-verbal creativity is concerned.

*Interaction effect of CTP with intelligence and sex (taken together) on the development of composite non-verbal creativity*

As revealed from the Table 16, the interaction of CTP with intelligence and sex (taken together) on the development of composite non-verbal creativity has also not come significant as the value of F-ratio (*i.e.*, 0.08) is far below to gain any significance. It means that the students of a particular sex having a particular level of intelligence does not influence the effect of CTP on the development of composite non-verbal creativity. In other words, it can be said that the programme is equally effective for both male and female students irrespective of their level of intelligence with regard to the development of composite non-verbal creativity.

(ii) *Reactions of the students towards creativity training programme (CTP)*

As already mentioned, the students of the treatment group who completed the training (N = 120) had been given an CTP questionnaire (Appendix-H) at the end of the experiment to find out their reactions towards the CTP. The reactions of these students were analyzed in terms of the percentage of their various responses for each statement. The summary of the analysis of these responses is given in Table 18.

**Table 18: Showing the percentage of the responses of the students in the treatment group on the various statements of the CTP questionnaire**

1. Do you feel that your creative thinking has improved after undergoing through this creativity training programme.

| | | |
|---|---|---|
| 1.66 | 21.67 | 76.67 |
| Not at all | a little | very much |

2. Do you enjoy using your mind more than you did before you began getting training through CTP.

| | | |
|---|---|---|
| 2.5 | 15.0 | 82.5 |
| No change | little more | much |

3. Do you feel that this training in creative thinking has helped you in your regular studies of the school.

| | | |
|---|---|---|
| 1.67 | 35.00 | 63.33 |
| Not at all | a little | very much |

4. Do you feel that this training in creative thinking has made your school

work more interesting.

| | | |
|---|---|---|
| 1.67 | 22.50 | 75.83 |
| No change | a little | a lot |

5. Do you feel that this training in creative thinking would somewhere help you while thinking for something new.

| | | |
|---|---|---|
| 2.50 | 22.50 | 75.00 |
| Not at all | a little | very much |

6. How did you like the training which you got through this creativity training programme.

| | | |
|---|---|---|
| 4.17 | 12.50 | 83.33 |
| Boring | Interesting | very interesting |

7. How did you like the exercises which you solved during training in creative thinking.

| | | |
|---|---|---|
| 5.83 | 35.00 | 59.17 |
| Very difficult | easy | very easy |

8. Would you like that this type of training in creative thinking should be given in the school every day like the study of other subjects.

| | |
|---|---|
| 4.17 | 95.83 |
| No | Yes |

9. Would you like that this type of training in creative thinking should be given more to you.

| | |
|---|---|
| 2.5 | 97.5 |
| No | Yes |

10. Would you like that these types of exercises related to creative thinking should be given in each subject:

| | |
|---|---|
| 4.17 | 95.83 |
| No | Yes |

From the Table 18, it is revealed that—

1. Quite a good number of students (76.67 per cent) felt that they have very much improved their creative thinking after undergoing training through this programme. However, some students (21.67 per cent) were of the opin-

ion that the improvement has been only a little. There were only very few students (1.66 per cent) who felt that their creative thinking has not improved at all.

With these reactions of the students, it appears that the creativity training programme had been successful in improving creative thinking of the majority of the students.

2. A large number of the student (82.5 per cent) reported that they now enjoy using their mind much more than they used to did before training. There were only some students (15.00 per cent) who found training enjoying only a little more. However, few students (2.5 per cent) did not found any change.

   It seems that the creativity training programme has also added to the joy of thinking for most of the students.

3. About 63.33 per cent students felt that the training has helped them very much in their regular studies of the school also. While only 35 per cent student found it helpful only a little, 1.67 per cent students felt that the training did not help them at all.

   It looks that the creativity training programme has also been helpful for quite good number of students in their regular studies of the school.

4. Though 75.83 per cent students found that

the training has made their school work interesting a lot, 1.67 per cent felt no change. However, there were some students (22.50 per cent) who found their school work a little more interesting after training.

It indicates that the creativity training programme has made work interesting for most of the students.

5. Quite a larger number of students (75.00 per cent) felt that this training would help them very much while thinking for some thing new. Though 2.50 per cent students were of the opinion that it may not help at all, 22.50 per cent students expected to get help a little in this regard.

   These reactions of the students show that the training may help the students somewhere while thinking for something new.

6. For 83.33 per cent students, creativity training programme was very interesting, but 4.17 per cent students found it boring. There were only 12.50 per cent students who found it just interesting.

   It means that the creativity training programme was found to be interesting for the majority of the students.

7. The programme has been found very easy for 59.17 per cent students, though 5.83 per cent

students found it very difficult. There were only 35 per cent students who found it just easy.

Thus, it appears that the programme, by and large, was easy.

8. Most of the students (95.83 per cent) wanted that this type of training should be given to them every day like the study of the other subjects. However, few students (4.17 per cent) were not of this opinion.
9. Majority of the students (97.5 per cent) were favourably inclined towards having more training in creative thinking of this type. But, there were also few students (2.15 per cent) who did not want it any more.
10. Finally, a large number of students (95.83 per cent) were of the opinion that this type of training should be given to them in each subject; though 4.17 per cent students had the opinion just reverse to this.

**Foot Notes:**

1. J.P. Guilford, *Fundamental Statistics in Psychology and Education.* Fourth Edition, International Student Edition, McGraw-Hill Book Company, New York, 1956, p. 274.
2. Ibid., pp. 300-301.
3. B.J. Winer, *Statistical Principles in Experimental Design.* Second Edition, International Student Edition, McGraw Hill, Kogakusha Ltd., Tokyo, 1962, pp. 205-206.
4. J.P. Guilford. *Fundamental Statistics in Psychology and Education,* Fourth Edition. International Student Edition, McGraw-Hill Book Comany, New York, 1956, p. 301.
5. J.P. Guilford. *Fundamental Statistics in Psychology and Education.* Fourth Edition. International Student Edition, McGraw-Hill Book Company, New York, 1956, p. 301.

# six

## FINDINGS AND EDUCATIONAL IMPLICATIONS

In order to achieve the objectives of the present study, the investigator had developed a "Creativity Training Programme (CTP)" whose effectiveness was tested by conducting an experiment on VI grade children as described in the third chapter. Further, the previous chapter, in this connection, discussed the analysis and interpretation of the data. It becomes, therefore, necessary to summarize the findings, conclusions and educational implications of the study resulting from this investigation. The present chapter is devoted to this purpose in the heads as given below:

### Finding of the Study

The following hypotheses were tested to arrive at the findings.

Hypothesis-$H_1$:

There is no significant difference in the mean gain

scores of verbal fluency between the students of the treatment group who are given training through CTP and the students of the non-treatment group who did not get such training.

With regard to the hypothesis stated above, the value of F (127.23) was found to be highly significant at .01 level. It leads to the rejection of the null hypothesis with 99 per cent confidence level. Further, the mean gain score of the students in the treatment group (20.27) was also found to be quite greater than the students of the non-treatment group (4.38) which shows that the students who had training through CTP improved their verbal fluency as against the students in the non-treatment group.

Hypothesis-$H_{1.1.}$:

There is no significant interaction of the level of intelligence with CTP on the development of verbal fluency.

Research findings in connection of this hypothesis is that the interaction between intelligence and CTP is insignificant as F-ratio does not reach to the significant value even at .05 level. Thus, the null hypothesis is accepted. It means that the level of intelligence of the students does not influence the effect of creativity training programme in developing verbal fluency.

Hypothesis-$H_{1.2.}$:

There is no significant interaction of sex with CTP

on the development of verbal fluency.

The null hypothesis in this case also is accepted as the F-value (1.70) is not significant. It means that the programme is equally effective for both male and female students in developing their verbal fluency.

Hypothesis-$H_{1.3}$:

There is no significant interaction of the level of intelligence and sex (combined) with CTP on the development of verbal fluency.

This hypothesis too is accepted as F-value (0.78) was found to be quite insignificant. It means that the programme does not have differential effect for a particular sex having a particular level of intelligence with regard to the development of verbal fluency.

Hypothesis-$H_2$:

There is no significant difference in the mean gain scores of verbal flexibility between the students of the treatment group who are given training through CTP and the students of the non-treatment group who did not get such training.

Research findings in connection of this hypothesis is that the value of F-ratio (31.13) is highly significant. Thus, null hypothesis is totally rejected. Furthermore, the difference in the mean gain scores was found to be in the favour of treatment group. This mean that the creativity training programme is also effective in developing student's verbal flexibility.

Hypothesis-$H_{2.1.}$:

There is no significant interaction of the level of intelligence with CTP on the development of verbal flexibility.

The above null nypothesis in this case is accepted as the F-value (1.02) was not found to be significant even at .05 level. It means that the students of all the intelligence level get equally benefited from the programme in developing their verbal flexibility also.

Hypothesis-$H_{2.2.}$:

There is no significant interaction of sex with CTP on the development of verbal flexibility.

The insignificant value of F (0.23) accepts this hypothesis also thereby giving the conclusion that both male and female students improve their verbal flexibility equally after they undergo training through the programme.

Hypothesis-$H_{2.3}$:

There is no significant interaction of the level of intelligence and sex (combined) with CTP on the development of verbal flexibility.

In this case also, the null hypothesis is accepted

owing to the low value of F (1.46) which is quite insignificant at .05 level. It concludes that the programme is equally effective for both male and female students irrespective of their intelligence level with regard to the development of verbal flexibility also.

Hypothesis-$H_3$:

There is no significant difference in the mean gain scores of verbal originality between the students of the treatment group who are given training through CTP and the students of the non-treatment group who did not get such training.

For this hypothesis, the value of F (51.94) was found to be highly significant at .01 level. It suggests the rejection of the null hypothesis. Further, the greater mean score of the students in the treatment group leads to the conclusion that the programme is effective in developing student's verbal originality.

Hypothesis-$H_{3.1.}$:

There is no significant interaction of the level of intelligence with CTP on the development of verbal originality.

The research findings in this case is that F-ratio (4.59) is significant at .05 level. Thus, null hypothesis is rejected at 95 per cent confidence level. It means that there is an influence of the level of intelligence on the effect of CTP in developing verbal originality. In other words, the programme exerted differential effect on the students of varying intelligence level.

Further, the creativity training programme seems to be more effective in developing verbal originality of the students of high and average intelligence level as compared to the students of low intelligence level because t-value (*i.e.*, 3.40 and 3.64) were found to be significant at .01 level for the students of the high and average intelligence level. However, the programme appears to be effective for the students of low intelligence level also as the t-value, though no significant, is high enough for this group too.

Hypothesis-$H_{3.2}$:

There is no significant interaction of sex with CTP on the development of verbal originality.

The insignificant value of F (*i.e.*, 3.05) leads us to accept this hypothesis thereby indicating that the programme is equally effective for both male and female children in developing their verbal originality. But as the value of F, though insignificant as stated, is quite high, it appears that the programme is more effective for a particular sex. Further, it has been found that the difference of the mean gain scores is more in the case of male students as compared to the female by 8.25 points. With this finding, it looks that male students benefited more than female students in developing their verbal originality.

Hypothesis-$H_{3.3.}$:

There is no significant interaction of the level of intelligence and sex (combined) with CTP on the development of verbal originality.

Research findings in case of this hypothesis is that the F-ratio (*i.e.*, 1.16) is not significant. Thus, the null hypothesis is accepted. It means that the programme is equally effective in developing verbal originality for both male and female students irrespective of their level of intelligence.

Hypotehsis-$H_4$:

There is no significant difference in the mean gain scores of composite verbal creativity between the students of the treatment group who are given training through CTP and the students of the non-treatment group who did not get such training.

This hypothesis is totally rejected at .01 level because of the highly significant value of F-ratio (*i.e.*, 138.12). Further, the difference of the mean gain scores (*i.e.*, 25.17 points) in the favour of treatment group indicates that the programme has been quite successful in developing the composite verbal creativity of the students.

Hypothesis-$H_{4.1.}$:

There is no significant interaction of the level of intelligence with CTP on the development of complete verbal creativity.

The value of F-ratio (*i.e.*, 0.76) for this hypothesis has been found very low which is quite insignificant even at .05 level. Thus, the null hypothesis stated above is accepted. It means that there is no interaction between intelligence and CTP as far as the development of composite verbal creativity is concerned. It appears, therefore, that intelligence does not interfere with CTP in developing composite verbal creativity in students.

Hypothesis-$H_{4.2}$:

There is no significant interaction of sex with CTP on the development of composite verbal creativity.

For this hypothesis also, the F-value (*i.e.*, 2.78) is insignificant. Thus, null hypothesis in this case also is accepted thereby indicating no interaction between sex and CTP. But, as the value of F, though not significant, is quite high, it appears that the programme has been more effective for a particular sex in developing composite verbal creativity.

Further, the difference in the mean gain scores has been found in the favour of male students by 3.67 points which increases the probability that male children are likely to get benefited more from CTP than female children in developing their composite verbal creativity.

Hypothesis-$H_{4.3}$:

> There is no significant interaction of the level of intelligence and sex (combined) with CTP on the development of composite verbal creativity of the students.

The value of F (*i.e.*, 1.25) has been found insignificant at .05 level for this hypothesis too. Thus, null hypothesis in this case too is accepted. It seems that the programme has been equally effective in developing composite verbal creativity for both male and female students irrespective of their level of intelligence. In other words, it can be said that the effect of CTP on the development of composite verbal originality has not been influenced with the students of a particular sex having a particular intelligence level.

Hypothesis-$H_5$:

> There is no significant difference in the mean gain scores of non-verbal originality between the students of the treatment group who are given training through CTP and the students of the non-treatment group who did not get such training.

Research findings for this hypothesis is that the value of F-ratio (*i.e.*, 54.61) is highly significant at .01 level. Thus, the null hypothesis is totally rejected. Furthermore, the mean gain score of the students in the treatment group was found to be greater by 4.35 points than the mean gain score of the students in the non-treatment group. It indicates that the creativity training programme is effective in developing non-verbal originality of the students.

Hypothesis-$H_{5.1}$:

There is no significant interaction of the level of intelligence with CTP on the development of non-verbal originality.

The value of F-ratio (*i.e.*, 0.78) is insignificant for this hypothesis. Thus, null hypothesis is accepted which indicates that there is no interaction between intelligence and CTP with regard to the development of non-verbal originality. It seems, therefore, that the level of intelligence does not influence the effect of CTP in developing non-verbal originality.

Hypothesis-$H_{5.2}$:

There is no significant interaction of sex with CTP on the development of non-verbal originality.

This hypothesis is also accepted as the value of F-ratio (0.036) was found to be quite insignificant. It means that the programme is equally effective for both male and female students in developing their non-verbal originality.

Hypothesis-$H_{5.3}$:

There is no significant interaction of the level of intelligence and sex (combined) with CTP on the development of non-verbal originality.

The null hypothesis in this case too is accepted as the F-value (0.69) is not significant. It means that the programme does not have differential effect for a particular sex having a particular level of intelligence with regard to the development of non-verbal originality.

Hypothesis-$H_6$:

There is no significant difference in the mean gain scores of non-verbal elaboration between the students of the treatment group who are given training through CTP and the students of the non-treatment group who did not get such training.

Research findings for this hypothesis is that the value of F-ratio (43.11) is highly significant. Thus, the null hypothesis is totally rejected. Furthermore, the difference in the mean gain scores was found to be in favour of the treatment group. It shows that the students who had training through CTP improved their non-verbal elaboration as against the students in the non-treatment group.

Hypothesis-$H_{6.1.}$:

There is no significant interaction of the level of intelligence with CTP on the development of non-verbal elaboration.

The value of F-ratio (0.24) for this hypothesis has been found very low which is quite insignificant even at .05 level. Thus, the null hypothesis is accepted. It means that the level of intelligence of the students does not influence the effect of creativity training programme in developing non-verbal elaboration in students.

Hypothesis-$H_{6.2}$:

There is no significant interaction of sex with CTP on the development of non-verbal elaboration.

The null hypothesis in this case also is accepted as the F-value (0.40) has not been found significant even at .05 level. It means that the programme is equally effective for both male and female students in developing their non-verbal elaboration.

Hypothesis-$H_{6.3.}$:

There is no significant interaction of the level of intelligence and sex (combined) with CTP on the development of non-verbal elaboration.

This hypothesis too is accepted as the value of F-ratio (0.12) was found to be quite insignificant. It appears that the programme is equally effective for both male and female students irrespective of their intelligence level as far as the development of non-verbal elaboration is concerned.

Hypothesis-$H_7$:

There is no significant difference in the mean gain scores of composite non-verbal creativity between the students of the treatment group who are given training through CTP and the students of the non-treatment group who did not get such training.

Research finding for this hypothesis is that the value of F-ratio (85.52) is highly significant. Thus, the null hypothesis is totally rejected. Further, the mean gain score of the students in the treatment group (53.20) was found to be quite greater than the students of the non-treatment group (19-17). It shows that the students who had training through CTP improved their composite non-verbal creativity as against the student in the non-tre..:ment group.

Hypothesis-$H_{7.1}$:

There is no significant interaction of the level of intelligence with CTP on the development of composite non-verbal creativity.

With regard to the hypothesis stated above, the value of F-ratio (0.87) was not found to be significant even at .05 level. Thus, null hypothesis is accepted. It indicates that there is no interaction between intelligence and CTP. It seems, therefore, that intelligence does not interfere with CTP in developing the composite non-verbal creativity.

Hypothesis-$H_{7.2}$:

There is no significant interaction of sex with CTP on the development of composite non-verbal creativity.

For this hypothesis also, the value of F-ratio (0.30) is insignificant. Thus, the null hypothesis in this case also is accepted. It indicates that the programme is equally effective for both male and female students in developing their composite non-verbal creativity.

Hypothesis-$H_{7.3}$:

There is no significant interaction of the level of intelligence and sex (combined) with CTP on the development of non-verbal creativity.

This hypothesis too is accepted as the value of F-ratio (0.08) was found to be quite low and so insignificant. It seems that the programme has been equally effective in developing composite non-verbal creativity for both male and female students irrespective of their level of intelligence. In other words, it can be said that the effect of CTP on the development of composite non-verbal creativity has not been influenced with the students of a particular sex having a particular level of intelligence.

**Conclusion and Discussion**

We are now in a position to draw some conclusions on the basis of the findings resulted from the hypothesis tested above. The same is discussed as given below:

In general, the findings of this research study given the conclusion that the creativity training programme (CTP) has been successful in developing creative thinking abilities in students. The students of the treatment group had significantly greater gain scores for all the components of verbal creativity (*viz.*, verbal fluency, flexibility, and originality) and non-verbal creativity (*viz.*, non-verbal originality and elaboration) as well as for the composite verbal and non-verbal creativity than the students of non-treatment group.

(i) For verbal fluency, flexibility and originality as well as for composite verbal creativity, these findings are consistent with the findings of the previous research studies employing other creativity training materials (Bahlke, 1967; Britton, 1967; Huber *et al.*, 1969; Feldhusen, Bahlke, and Treffinger, 1969; Reese and Parnes, 1970; Woodliff, 1970; Feldhusen, Treffinger, and Thomas, 1971; Speedie, Treffinger, and Feldhusen, 1971; Shively *et al.*, 1972; Khatena and Dickerson, 1973; Moreno and Hogan, 1976; Ford and Renjulli, 1976; Alencer, Feldhusen and Widlak, 1976; Jeanne, 1981; Jarial, 1982).

Thus, creativity training programme (CTP) developed by the investigator, like other creativity training material, seems to be an effective instructional programme for developing the various components of verbal creativity and as well as composite verbal creativity.

(ii) With regard to non-verbal originality, elaboration and composite non-verbal creativity also, the findings of this study are in agreement with the findings of other researchers (Britton, 1967; Feldhusen, Bahlke and Treffinger, 1969; Reese and Parnes, 1970; Ford and Renjulli, 1976; Alencer *et al.*, 1976; Jeanne, 1981;

and Jarial, 1982).

This comparative analysis indicates that this creativity training programme (CTP), like other programmes, is also effective in developing the various components of non-verbal creativity as well as composite non-verbal creativity.

(iii) As far as the interaction of the level of intelligence with the creativity training programme (CTP) on the development of various components of verbal and non-verbal creativity and composite verbal and non-verbal creativity is concerned, the findings of the present study do not indicate any significant interaction between intelligence level and CTP except for verbal originality. These findings are consistent with the results of the previous research studies conducted by Covington and Crutchfield (1965), Olton *et al.* (1967), Wardrop *et al.* (1969), Olton and Crutchfield (1969), Huber *et al.* (1979), Deshmukh (1980) and Tweet (1981).

Thus, it appears that the programme is equally effective for the students of all intelligence level in developing various components of creativity except for verbal originality. Furthermore, as already stated, the present study has revealed that the students of high intelligence level improved their verbal originality more through CTP than the students of average intelligence level, who in turn, improved more than the students of low intelligence level. Thus, it seems that the creativity training programme (CTP) developed by the investigator has been more effective for the students of high and average intelligence level as compared to the students of low intelligence level.

The presence of a significant interaction between intelligence and CTP for verbal originality might have been influenced by several factors. One of the factors might have been that the CTP exercises would have been more attractive and interesting to the students of high and average intelligence level than for the students of low intelligence level in producing more gains for verbal originality (Huber, *et al.*, 1979)[1].

(iv) Concerning the intereaction of sex with CTP too, the findings of this study are consistent with the results of earlier researches (Tweet, 1981; Jarial, 1982) which indicates no interaction between sex and creativity training. Thus, it can be said that, like other studies, the CTP is equally effective for both male and female students.

(v) As no interaction has been found among the level of intelligence, sex and CTP for any of the component of creativity, it appears that the CTP is equally effective for both male and female students irrespective of their level of intelligence in developing the various components of verbal and non verbal creativity and the composite verbal and non-verbal creativity. In other words, it can be said that the CTP does not have differential effect for a particular sex having a particular level of intelligence for any of the component of creativity. The investigator could not trace out any previous study which have studied the interaction among the intelligence level, sex and creativity training to compare the findings of this study. It is, therefore, suggested that some more research studies are conducted with regard to this question before arriving at some final conclusion.

(vi) Some conclusions can also be drawn from the reactions of the students towards creativity training programme. Majority of the students felt that they have improved their creative thinking skills, have come to enjoy using their minds more than before, and were favourably inclined towards further training in creative thinking. Most of the students also felt that the training through CTP has helped them in their regular studies of the school, has made their school work more interesting and would somewhere help them while thinking for some thing new. A large number of students found the training very easy and interesting too. Almost all the students were of the opinion that this type of training should be given in the school every day like the study of the other subjects and also in each subject.

It seems that the creativity training programme has been successful in leaving a favourable impact on the minds of the students as evident from their opinion.

## Educational Implications

Like other research studies, the findings of this investigation also have potential educational implications. This study re-affirms the development of creative potential in school children as one of the important objective of education which has been neglected from the very beginning in our educational system.

To start with, the study first of all has projected some clarifications about some of the misconceptions with regard to the creativity which we most of us earlier had. One of the common belief among teachers and parents had been that the child will become creative of his own accord. The development of creativity is not a matter of chance as Torrance somewhere stated. In order to develop creative thinking in children deliberate attempts are necessary. It means that the creativity is not just the by-product of our present educational system, rather a special type of education is needed which gives exclusive attention to the development of creativity.

Second wrong notion had been that a nurturing environment alone can help children to develop their creative potential. It is true that a stimulating environment does play a role in enhancing creative capacity of child but this is only a part of the whole story. An nurturing environment alone can not help children to develop their creative potential because it can not supply what the person basically lacks. In order to develop creative thinking abilities, a child must have a reportoire of creative thinking skills at his disposal. In other words he must learn how to think creativity and what constitute the creativity thinking. It suggests that education must evolve a wayout to fix those skills in the reportoire of child which help him to think in a creative way.

One more misconception among most of us is that we believe that creative achievement is a matter of how much creative potential a person is endowed with. This study suggests that the development of creative potential is of much importance than the mere possession of it. What is possessed is useless if it is not capable of being expressed. Experssion of any potential needs its proper develcpment. Thus, it indicates that there exist a pronounced gap between creative potential and creative performance and this gap can be narrowed by deliberate education in creative thinking.

The creativity training programme (CTP) described in this study produced substantial gains in the creative thinking skills of VI grade children as compared to those children who did not get the experience of this programme and were studying in their regular class room as usual. The fact that these substantial gains could be produced by a programme of modest proportions suggests that the existing schools programmes are doing less than what they should do in teaching students how to think creatively. If the schools were being more effective in this regard, it is unlikely that such a modest programme would have had such impressive effects. Therefore, if the schools intend to make effective progress toward the newly emphasized goal of teaching the student "how to think" rather than merely teaching him "what to think", new educational programme must be designed to provide extensive and systematic instruction in creative thinking skills for all the students at all grade levels.

One of the major implication of the study is that it has provided the evidences that the creative potential in children is capable of being developed through appropriate education and training. The earlier notion that the creative potential is merely hereditarial seems no more valid. Heredity does not place limits upon creative development and achievement. Creative abilities are inherited to the extent that a person inherits his sense organs, nervous system and brain. How these abilities develop and function however is strongly influenced by the way education responds to his curiosity and creative needs. It suggests that we can certainly chalk out a such type of systematic programme of education which could help the children to develop their creative potential upto the optimum level.

The study has also highlighted the fact that creative thinking abilities are a kind of skills which can be trained by providing practice with the help of appropriate instructional material. Such instructional material can be developed in each subject which provide the children opportunity to improve their creative thinking power also along with the other faculties of mind. For this, a drastic change is needed in the curriculum and in the way of presentation of content material in the books prescribed for the students.

Another most important implication of the present study is that it has become clear that creative thinking can be developed without making major changes in the basic cognitive capacities of the students. Gain produced in a relatively short period of time imply that the instructional programme did not achieve its effects by changing the basic cognitive capacities of the student. Rather it seems likely that the programme showed the student how to make for more effective use of the cognitive capacities he already had. Thus, instead of developing entirely new and different cognitive capacities, such instructional material can be prepared and used which help the children to make the effective use of the cognitive capacities he already had.

The study points out one more important fact that most of the children are unable to show their creative performance because they don't know 'how to think creatively'. If the students are explained the various ways and steps which are involved in creative thinking and are asked to use them by solving creative thinking exercises, it can be expected that they would be able to think in more creative ways than otherwise. It also suggests that the children should be given direct training in creative thinking. Here, a problem arises how? One may be that the teacher himself teaches the subject matter in a way that it involves creative thinking on the part of the students. Another way may be that the students are given such exercises to do at home or in the class room itself which compel them to think divergently.

The results of this study have also shown that creative ability is not the monopoly of the favoured few. The students of average and even low level of intelligence demonstrated an improvement in their creativity level after training through CTP. It suggests that the children of all intelligence level can improve their creative thinking level, if they are given chance through appropriate education and training. It would be wrong to assume that the only highly intelligent children can be creative as most of the teacher generally think. It has been observed that the teachers always like the intelligent children and neglect those children who are less intelligent. By doing so, in fact, they ignore a large number of student population to come up with their creative potential and hence a lot of creative potential remains uncared. It is here that this study suggest that all the children should be treated equally irrespective of their intelligence level if we want to flourish their creativity.

The study, thus, makes clear that the level of intelligence has not to do much with creative performance. What is more important than the level of intelligence is the effectiveness with which a person uses it for his creative performance. Therefore, it seems that the children of all intelligence level are equally capable of developing their creative potential. Though, the study has also revealed that the students of high intelligence level develop their verbal originality more than the students of average intelligence level, who in turn, develop more than the students of low intelligence level. It does not mean that this type of training in creative thinking is not beneficial for the students of low intelligence level. Gain obtained by the students of low intelligence level as a result of creativity training has clearly indicated that the students of even low intelligence level can improve their creative thinking skills. However, some special type of creativity training material may be prepared for those children who are low in their intelligence level so that it can help them to develop their creative thinking in a more better way.

The study has also shown that there is no interaction between creativity training programme and sex. It indicates that both boys and girls develop their creative thinking abilities equally. In other words the improvement is not greater in either boys or girls. This finding reveals that all the children, irrespective of their sex, are capable to develop their creative potential. It suggests that the education should look to both the sex equally as far as the development of creative thinking is concerned. The education can produce equal number of creative persons from both the sex.

To conclude it can be said that though creativity can not be produced but it can certainly be nourished. Vervalin (1962)[2] has even said that creativity can be learned by those persons for whom it does not come naturally. Therefore, it seems that the systematic programmes for teaching the student how to think creatively should be one of the central concerns of education at all levels and for all types of children. By providing such education, if every member of the human family could be made even a little more creative, in summation the benefits could be tremendous. Thus, it is hoped that this study will go a long way to open a new area in the field of education whereby the creative potential of our school children can properly be nourished.

Foot Notes:

1. J. Huber, D. Treffinger, and D. Tracy. Self-instructional use of programmed creativity-training material with gifted and regular students. *Journal of Educational Psychology,* 1979, Vol. 71, No. 3, p. 307.
2. C.H. Vervalin (1962). How you can develop a creative Imagination. In G.A. Davis; and J.A. Scott (Editors). *Training Creative Thinking,* Holt, Rinehart and Winston, Inc., New York, 1971.

**Bibliography:**

Acharyalu, S.T.V.G. Creativity: Its need in Indian Education. In Rais Ahmed (Editor). *Creativity and Undergraduate Science Education.* Proceedings of a Seminar, Aligarh Muslim University, Aligarh, 1972, pp. 7.13.

Ahmed, Rais (Editor). Creativity and Undergraduate Science Education. *Proceedings of a Seminar held at the department* of Physics, Aligarh Muslim University, Aligarh, February, 10-12, 1972.

Ahmed, R. and Jafri, A.V. An Experiment in Creative Teaching. *The Educational Trends,* 1973, Vol. 8, pp. 97-101.

Akinboye, J.O. An experimental Study of the Effectiveness of Brain Storming in Small Groups of Nigerian Subjects. *Journal of Creative Behaviour.* 1980, Vol. 14, No. 1, p. 268.

Alencer, E. and Soranode, E. A Study of Creativity Training in Elementary Grades in Brazilian Schools. *Dissertation Abstracts,* 1971, Vol. 35, No. 6, p. 3502-A.

Alencer, E., Feldhusen, J.F., and Widlak, F.W. Creativity training in Elementary Schools in Brazil. *Journal of Experimental Education,* 1976, Vol. 44, No. 4, pp. 23-26.

Amram, F.M., and Clese, L. Identifying and teaching creativity. *Research in Education,* 1965, Vol. 3, No. 6, p. 87.

Anastasi, A. and Schaefer, C.E. Note on the concepts of creativity and intelligence. *Journal of Creative Behaviour.* 1971, Vol. 5, No. 1, pp. 113-116.

Anderson, H.H. *Creativity and Its Cultivation.* New York: Harper, 1959.

Anderson, H.H. Creativity and Education. *Educational Horizons.* Winter, 1961-62, pp. 123-129.

Anderson, H.H. (Editor). *Creativity in childhood and adolescence: A variety of approaches.* Palo Alto, California: Science and Behaviour Books, 1965.

Arieti, S. *Creativity: The magic synthesis.* New York: Basic Books, 1976.

Aschner, Mary J. and Blish, C.E. (Eds.) *Productive thinking in education.* Washington: National Education Association, 1965.

Bachtold Louise M. and Wesner, Emmy, E. An evaluation of teaching creative skills to gifted students in grades V. and VI. *Journal of Educational Research,* 1970, Vol. 63, No.6, pp. 253-256.

Behlke, S.J. A study of the enhancement of creative abilities in elementary school children. *Unpublished Master's Thesis.* Purdue University, 1967.

Ball, Orlow Fugene. The effects of transcendental meditation (TM) and TM sidhis programme on verbal and figural creativity (TTCT), auditory creativity and hemispheric dominance (SOLAT). *Dessertation Abstracts,* 1980, Vol. 40. No. 1, p. 3880-A.

Barron, F. The Psychology of Creativity. In *Encyclopaedia Britannica,* New York, Inc., 1963, pp. 711-712.

Barron, F. *The Creative Person and the Creative Process,* N.Y., Holt, 1969.

Basu, C.K. and Jawa, Sarla. A Factor Analytical Study of Torrance Tests of Creative Thinking. *Creativity News letter,* 1973, Vol. 11, pp. 21-26.

Bhalke, S.J. Compotential evaluation of creativity instructional materials. *Dissertation Abstracts.* 1969, Vol. 30, p. 1425-A.

Bhan, R. Social factors in creative potentiality, *Manas,* 1970, Vol. 71, No.1, pp. 21-27.

Bhaskar, S. Studies of the effectiveness of verbal creativity instructional material at school stage. *Unpublished Doctoral Dissertation,* M.S. University, Baroda, 1982.

Blankenship, Dallas James. A study of the effects of creativity training upon the self concept, achievement and creative performance of first grade pupils. *Dissertation Abstracts,* 1976, Vol. 36, p. 7167-A.

Bonsall, M.R. Current school programmes for developing creativity. In French, J.L. (Ed.) *Educating the Gifted,* New York, Holt, 1964.

Boutte, Margarat. The effect of cognitive behaviour modification on enhancing creativity. *Dissertation Abstracts,* 1980, Vol. 40, p. 5783-A.

Brown, G.I. An experiment in the teaching of creativity. *School Review,* 1965, Vol. 93, p. 4.

Bruch, C.B. Increasing children's creativity through a combination of teacher training approaches. *The Gifted Child Quarterly,* 1965, Vol. 9, pp. 24-28.

Bruner, J.S. The conditions of creativity. In H.E. Gruber, G. Terrell and M. Wertheimer (Editors), *Contemporary Approaches to Creative Thinking,* N.Y., Atherton Press, 1962.

Buch, M.B. (Editor). *A Survey of Research in Education,* Baroda, CASE, M.S. University, 1973.

Buch, M.B. (Editor), *Second Survey of Research in Education,* CASE, M.S. University, Baroda, 1979.

Burt, C. The Psychology of Creative ability. *British Journal of Educational Psychology,* 1962, Vol. 32, pp. 292-298.

Butcher, H.J. *Human Intelligence: Its nature and assessments.* London, Methuen and Co., 1968.

Butcher, H.J. Recent research into creativity and divergent thinking in Great Britain. *Journal of Research and Development in Education,* 1971, Vol. 4, No.3, pp. 109-112.

Callahan, C.M. The effects of the connecticut mark-1 creativity programme on creative thinking of VI grade children. *Dissertation Abstracts,* 1973, Vol. 34, No.1, p. 1689-A.

Callahan, Carolyn M., and Renjulli, Joseph S. Development and evaluation of a creativity training programme. *Excep-*

*tional children,* Sept., 1974, Vol. 41, No. 1, pp. 44-45.

Callahan, C.M. and Renjulli, J.S. The effectiveness of a creativity training programme in the language arts. *The Gifted Child Quarterly,* Winter, 1977, Vol. 21, No. 4, pp. 538-545.

Casey, A.M. The effects of using a work book approach in teaching divergent thinking to six grade pupils. *Master Research paper.* Carnell University, 1965.

Caspi, M. Towards creative education. *Educational Issues.* Hebrew University, Jerusalem, 1972, Vol. 4, pp. 7-33.

Castelli, O.D. An exploration of the relationship between teacher's creative ability and teacher-pupil creative behaviour. *Dissertation Abstracts,* 1964, Vol. 25, p. 3320-A.

Chambers, J.A. Beginning a multi-dimension theory of creativity. *Psychological Report,* 1969, Vol. 25, No. 3, pp. 779-799.

Cherry, B.S. A strategy for developing creative thinking (Torrance Model) in trainable mentally retarded children through a programme of attention, concentration and open-ended methods. *Dissertation Abstract,* 1973, Vol. 33, pp. 4975-76-A.

Christe, T.C. The environmental factors in creativity. *Journal of creative Behaviour,* 1970, Vol. 4, No. 1, pp. 13-31.

Clark, B.M., and Trowbridge, N. Encouraging creativity through inservice teacher education. *Journal of Research and Development in Education,* 1971, Vol. 4, No. 3, pp. 87-94.

Cochran, W.G. and G.M. Cox. *Experimental Design.* New York, John Wiley and Sons, Inc., 1950.

Covington, M.V., and Crutchfied, R.S. Facilitation of Creative problem solving. *Programmed Instruction,* 1965, Vol. 4, No. 10, pp. 3-5.

Covington, M.V., and Crutchfield, R.S. Experiment in the use of programmed instruction for the facilitation of creative problem solving. *Programmed Instruction,* 1965, Vol. 4, pp. 3-10.

Covington, M.V., Crutchfield, R.S., and Davis, L.B. *The Productive Thinking Programme.* Berkelye, California: Brazelton Printing Co., 1966.

Covington, M.V. Promoting Creative thinking. *Journal of Experimental Education,* 1968, Vol. 37, No. 1, pp. 22-30.

Covington, M.V., Crutchfield, R.S., Davis, L., and Olton, R.M. *The productive thinking programme: A course in learning to think.* Clumbus, Chio: Merrill, 1974.

Crabtree, C. Effects of structuring on the productiveness of children's thinking. *Journal of Experimental Education,* 1967, Vol. 36, pp. 1-13.

Crawford, R.T. *The technique of creative thinking,* New York, Hawthorne Books, Inc., 1954.

Cropley, A.J. Creativity and Intelligence. *British Journal of Educational Psychology.* 1966, Vol. 36, pp. 259-266.

Croopley, A.J. Creativity: A new kind of intellect. *Australian Journal of Education,* 1967, Vol. 11, pp. 120-25 (b).

Croopley, A.J. *Creativity.* London, Longmans, Green and Co., 1967.

Croopley, A.J., and Feuring, E. Training Creativity in young children. *Developmental Psychology,* 1971, Vol. 4, p. 105.

Croopley, A.J. Creativity and Culture. *The Educational Trends,* 1973, Vol. 8, No. 1-4, pp. 19-27.

Crutchfield, R.S. and Covington, M.V. Programmed Instruction and Creativity. *Programmed Instruction,* 1965, Vol. 4, No. 1, pp. 8-10.

Crutchfield, R.S. Creative thinking in children: Its teaching and testing. In Brim, H., Crutchfield, R.S., and Holtzman W. *Intelligence: Perspective,* 1965, New York: Harcourt, Brace and World, 1966, pp. 33-64.

Cunningham, B.F., Myers, R.E., and Torrance, E.P. *Imagi/Craft.* Massachusetts, Lexiton, Ginn and Company, 1965.

Cunninghum, B.F., and Torrance, E.P. *Sounds and Images.* Boston: Ginn and Company, 1965.

Dacey, J.S. Programmed instruction in creativity and its effects on eighth grade students (Doctoral Dissertation, Cornell University, 1967). *Dissertation Abstracts,* 1971, Vol. 32, p. 2479-A.

Davis, G.A., and Houtamann, S.E. *Thinking Creatively: A guide to training imagination,* Wisconsin, Research and development centre, University of Wisconsin, Madison, Wisconsin, 1968.

Davis, G.A. and Houtman, S.E., Thomas, F.W., and William, E.R. *A Programme for training creative thinking: I. Preliminary field test.* Madison, Wisconsin: Centre for Cognitive learning, University of Wisconsin, 1969.

Davis, Gary A., and Scott, Joseph A. (Editors). *Training Creative Thinking.* Holt, Rinehart and Winston, Inc., New York, 1971.

Davis, G.A. Training creativity in adolescents. In G.A. Davis and J.A. Scott. *Training Creative Thinking,* New York, Holt, Rinehart and Winston, Inc., 1971, pp. 261-269.

Deshmukh, M.N. Teachability of creativity. *Journal of Indian Education,* 1977, Vol. 3, No. 2.

Deshmukh, M.N. Educational technology for creative education. *Journal of Indian Education,* 1979, Vol. 5, No. 4, pp. 4-11.

Deshmukh, M.N. Multi-media approach to creative teaching: A retrospect. *Annual Magazine,* Vinod Pustak Mandir, Agra, 1983, pp. 51-54.

Deshmukh, M.N. *Creativity in class rooms,* Vikash Publishing House, New Delhi, 1984.

DeRoche, E.F. Creativity in the class room. *Journal of Creative*

*Behaviour,* 1968, Vol. 2, No. 4,

Drevdahl, J.E. Some developmental and environmental factors in creativity. In C.W. Taylor (Editor). *Widening Horizons in Creativity,* N.Y. Wiley, 1964.

Drews, Elizabeth. Profile of Creativity. *NEA Journal,* 1963, Vol. 52, No.1, pp. 26-28.

Dutt, N.K. *Psychological Foundations of Education,* Doaba House, Nai Sarak, New Delhi, 1975, pp. 219-225.

Dutt, N.K. and Lal, G. *Creative Potential and Education,* Indian Book Agency, Ambala Cantt. 1977, pp. 39-47.

Dye, M.E., An inquiry into creativity and its nurturing climate: An exploratory study. *Journal of Creative Behaviour,* 1967, Vol. 1, No.2, p. 208.

Ebel, R.L., Rogers, M.B., and Victor, H.N. (Editors). *Encyclopaedia of Educational Research,* Fourth Edition, Collier, Macmillan, London, 1969.

Eberle, R.f. *Experimentation in the teaching of the creative thinking process: A Research Report.* Edwardsville Junior High School, Edwardsville, Illinois, 1965.

Edwards, A.L. *Experimental Design in Psychological Research.* New Delhi, Amerind Publishing Co. Pvt. Ltd., 1971.

Edwards, M.O. A Survey of problem solving courses. *Journal of Creative Behaviour,* 1968, Vol. 2, pp. 33-51.

Ellinger, B. The Genesis of Creativity. *Reading Teacher,* 1966, Vol. 19, pp. 493-397.

Enoches, P.D. An experimental study of a method for developing creative thinking in V grade children. *Dissertation Abstracts,* 1965, Vol. 28, No. 8, pp. 4538-39-A.

Eugene, Jernald Johnson. Creativity teaching - its effect upon creative thinking ability, achievement and intelligence of selected fourth grade students. *Dissertation Abstracts,* 1975, Vol. 35, p. 4132-A.

Eyring, H. Scientific creativity. In H.H. Anderson (Ed.). *Creativity and Its Cultivation,* New York, Harper, 1959, pp. 10-11.

Feldhusen, J.F. *Programming and talented pupil.* Clearinghouse, 1963, Vol. 38, pp. 151-54.

Feldhusen, J.F., Bahlke, S.J., and Treffinger, D.J. Teaching Creative thinking. *Elementary School Journal.* 1969, Vol. 70, pp. 48-53.

Feldhusen, J.F., Elias, R.M., and Treffinger, D.J. The right kind of programmed instruction for the gifted and talented. *NSPH Journal.* 1969, Vol. 8, pp. 6-11.

Feldhusen, J.F. Treffinger, D.J. and Bahlke, S.J. Developing creative thinking: The Purdue Creativity Training Programme. *Journal of Creative Behaviour,* 1970, Vol. 4, No. 2, pp. 85-90.

Feldhusen, J. F.: Speedie, S.M., and Treffinger, D.J. The Purdue Creative thinking programme: Research and evaluation. *NSPI Journal,* 1971, Vol. 10, No. 3, pp. 5-9.

Feldhusen, J.F., Treffinger, D.J., and Thomas, S.J. *Global and Componential Evaluation of Creativity Training Materials.* (Creative Education Foundation Monograph). Buffalo, N.Y., Creative Education Foundation, State University College, 1971.

Fergusen, P.C. The meta-analysis of TM Programme. *Doctoral Dissertation,* School of Education, University of Colorado, Boulder, 1977.

Franklin, B.S., and Richards, P.N. Effects on children's divergent thinking abilities of a period of direct teaching for divergent production. *British Journal of Educational Psychology,* 1977, Vol. 47, pp. 66-70.

Freeman, J., Butcher, H.J., and Christie, T. Creativity: A selected review of research. London, *Society for Research into Higher Education,* 1971.

Freiheit, S.G. The effects of a training programme upon the creative performance of fourth grade children (*Technical Report No. 79*) University of Wisconsin, 1969.

Fromm, Erick. The creative attitude. In H.H. Anderson (Ed.) *Creativity and Its Cultivation,* N.Y. Harper and Row, 1959.

Fults, Elizabeth Ann. The effect of an instructional programme on the creative thinking skills, self concept, and leadership of intellectually and academically gifted elementary students. *Dissertation Abstract,* 1981, Vol. 41, No. 7, p. 2934-A.

Gallagher, J.J. *Teaching the Gifted Ghild.* Boston Allyn and Bacon, 1964.

Garret, H.E. *Statistics in Psychology and Education,* Vakils, Feffer and Simens Pvt. Ltd., Bombay, 1966.

Getzel, J.W. and Jackson, P.W. *Creativity and Intelligence,* New York, Wiley, 1962.

Getzels, J.W. Creative thinking, Problem solving, and instruction. In E.R. Hilgard (Ed.) *Theories of Learning and Instruction.* Chicago, University of Chicago Press, 1964, pp. 240-267.

Getzels, J.W. and Madaus, G.F. Creativity. In R.L. Ebel (Ed.) *Encyclopaedia of Educational Research* (4th ed.), New York: Macmillan, 1969, pp. 267-275.

Ghiselin, B. *The Creative Process,* Berkeley: University of California Press, 1952.

Gilchrist, M. *The Psychology of Creativity.* Carlton, Victoria: Melbourne University Press, 1972.

Glass, G.V. Intergrating findings: The meta-analysis of research. In L.S. Shulman (Ed.). *Review of Research in Education* (Vol. 5). Itasca, JL: 1976.

Goodale, R.A. Methods of encouraging creativity in the class room. *Journal of Creative Behaviour,* Vol. 4, No.2, pp. 91-102.

Goor, A., and Rapoport, T. Enhancing creativity in an informal educational framework. *Journal of Educational Psychology,* 1977, Vol. 69, pp. 636-643.

Gordon, W.J.J. Synetics: *The development of creative capacity,* New York; Harper, 1961.

Goulab, S. and Hahn, K.S. Training creative thinking in the open and traditional class rooms. *Journal of Creative Behavour,* 1983, Vol. 17, No. 3, p. 217.

Goyal, R.P. Creativity and School Climate: An exploratory study. *Journal of Psychological Researches,* 1973 (a), Vol. 17, No. 2, pp. 77-80.

Goyal, R.P. An investigation into the effect of differing school climates upon pupils' creativity. *Quest in Education,* 1975, Vol. 12, No.1.

Gowan, J.C., Demos, D.G., and Torrance, E.P. (Eds.) *Creativity: its educational implicating,* New York: John Wiley, 1967.

Gowan, J.C. What makes a creative child gifted? Four theories. In J.C. Gowan. G.D. Demos and E.P. Torrance, *Creativity: Its Educational Implications.* John Wiley, New York, 1967, pp. 9-15.

Gowan, J.C. *Development of the Creative Individual.* San Diego: Robert Knapp, 1972.

Gowan, J.C. The facilitation of creativity through meditational procedures. *Journal of Creative Behavour,* 1978, Vol. 12, No. 3, pp. 156-160.

Gray, W.W. An experimental study utilizing problem solving technique in IX grade health class. *Dissertation Abstract,* 1964, Vol. 25, No. 4, p. 2457-A.

Gruber, H.E., Terrill, G. and Wertheimer, M. (Eds.) *Contemporary Approaches to Creative Thinking.* New York: Atherton Press, 1963.

Guilford, J.P. Creativity. *American Psychologist,* 1950, Vol. 5, pp. 444-454.

Guilford, J.P. Structure of Intellect. *Psychological Bulletin.* 1956, Vol. 53, pp. 267-293.

Guilford, J.P. Traits of Creativity. In H.H. Anderson (Eds.) *Creativity and Its Cultivation,* New York, Harper, 1959, pp. 142-61.

Guilford, J.P. Three faces of intellect. *American Psychologist.* 1959 (a) Vol. 14, pp. 469-479.

Guilford, J.P. Creativity: Its measurement and development: In Parnes, S.J. and Harding H.F. *A Source Book for Creative Thinking,* New York: Charles Scribners Sons, 1962, pp. 151-58.

Guilford, J.P. Potentiality for Creativity. *Gifted Child Quarterly,* 1962, Vol. 6, pp. 87-90.

Guilford, J.P. Some theoretical views of creativity. In H. Helson and W. Bevaw (Eds.). *Contemporary Approaches to Psychology,* New York: Van Nostrand, 1964 (a).

Guilford, J.P. *Fundamental Statistics in Psychology and Education,* New York, McGraw Hill Book Company, 1965.

Guilford, J.P. A Psychometric approach to creativity. In H.H. Anderson (Ed.). *Creativity in Childhood and Adolescents,* California: Science and Behaviour Books, 1965.

Guilford, J.P. Basic Problems in Teaching for Creativity. In C.S. Taylor and F.E. Williams (Eds.) *Instructional Media and Creativity,* New York: Wiley, 1966, pp. 71-103.

Guilford, J.P. Frontiers in thinking that teachers should know about? In J.C. Gowan, G.D. Demons and E.P. Torrance (Editors). *Creativity: Its Educational Implications,* New York, John Wiley and Sons, 1967, pp. 150-157.

Guilford, J.P. Creativity: Yesterday, today and tomorrow. *Journal of Creative Behaviour,* 1967, Vol. 1, No.I, pp. 3-13.

Guilford, J.P. *Nature of Intelligence,* McGraw Hill, 1968.

Guilford, J.P. Creativity: Retrospect and prospect. *Journal of Creative Behaviour,* 1970, Vol. 4, pp. 149-168.

Guilford, J.P. and Hoepfner, R.L. *The Analysis of Intelligence,* New York, McGraw Hill, 1971, pp. 367-497.

Guilford, J.P. Some misconceptions regarding measurement of creative talent. *Journal of Creative Behaviour,* 1971, Vol. 5, pp. 77-87.

Guilford, J.P. Creativity: Dispositions and Processes. In M.K. Raina (Ed.), *Creativity Research: International Perspective,* New Delhi, NCERT, 1980, pp. 218-235.

Gupta, A.K. Creativity: Rotrospect and Prospect. *Journal of Creative Behaviour,* 1974, Vol. 3, No.1, pp. 18-24.

Gupta, A.K. *A Study of Class room Teaching Behaviour and Creativity.* Light and Life Publisher, New Delhi, 1980.

Gupta, P.K. Education for Creativity: A Global Issue. *NEHU Journal of Social Science and Humanities,* North Eastern Hill University Publications, Vol. 2, No. 1, pp. 27-30.

Haddon, F.A., and Lytton, H. Teaching approach and the development of divergent thinking abilties in primary schools. *British Journal of Educational Psychology.* 1988, Vol. 38, pp. 171-180.

Haddon, F.A., and Lytton, H. Techniques of creative teaching. *Journal of creative Behavour.* 1967, Vol. 1, No. 4, pp. 325-330.

Hallman, R.J. Can creativity be taught? *Educational Theory,* 1964, Vol. 14, pp. 15-23.

Hensel, N.H. The development, implementation and evaluation of creative dramatics programme for kindergarten children. University of Georgia. *Dissertation Abstracts,* 1973, Vol. 34, pp. 4562-A.

Heist, P. (Ed.) *Education for Creativity.* Berkeley: Centre for

Research and Development in Higher Education, 1967, pp. 1-20.

Hilgard, E.R. Creativity and Problem-solving. In H.H. Anderson (Ed.) *Creativity and its Cultivation,* New York, harper, 1952, pp. 162-180.

Hocevar, D. and Michael, W.B. The effects of scoring formula on the discriminant validity of tests of creative thinking. *Educational and Psychological Measurement,* Vol. 39, pp. 917-921.

Huber, J., Treffinger, D., Tracy Dick, and Rand, Dave. Self-instructional use of programmed creativity training material, with gifted and regular students. *Journal of Educational Psychology,* 1979, Vol. 71, No. 3, pp. 303-309.

Hudson, L. (1966). Question of creativity. In P.E. Vernon (Ed.) *Creativity.* Penguin Books Ltd., England, 1970.

Jalota, S.S. *Manual of Directions for the Group Test of General Mental Ability.* New Delhi, Psycho-Centre, 1964.

Johnson, E.J. Creative teaching—its effect upon the creative thinking ability, achievement and intelligence of selected fourth grade students. *Dissertation Abstracts,* 1975, Vol. 35, No. 1, p. 4132.

Johnes, Helen, The effects of a training programme for teachers upon the class room responding behaviour of teachers towards creative students behaviour. *Dissertation Abstracts,* 1980, Vol. 41, No. 3, p. 1028-A.

Jones, J.C. A Study of the effect of a teaching strategy in divergent thinking upon the behaviour of student teachers and the children they teach. *Dissertation Abstracts.* 1970, Vol. 30, p. 2231-A.

Khatena, J. A second study of training college adults to think creatively with words. *Psychological Reports,* 1971, Vol. 28, No. 2, pp. 385-86.

Khatena, J. Some problems in the measurement of creative behaviour. *Journal of Research and Development in Education.* 1971, Vol. 4, pp. 74-82.

Khatena, J. Teaching disadvantaged pre-school children to think creatively with pictures. *Journal of Educational Psychology,* 1971, Vol. 62, pp. 384-386.

Khatena, J. Creative level and its effects on training college adults to think creatively with words. *Psychological Reports,* 1973, Vol. 32, p. 336.

Khatena, J., and Dickerson, E.C. Training sixth grade children to think creatively. *Psychological Reports,* 1973, 32, 841-842.

Khatena, J. Creativity: thought and study in the United States and Abroad. In M.K. Raina (Ed.) *Creadivity Research: International Perspective,* New Delhi, NCERT., 1980, pp. 282-204.

Khire, Usha. Education for creativity. *Journal of Indian Education,*1977, Vol. 3, No. 3., pp. 26-30.

Kneller, G.F. *The Act and Science of Creativity,* New York, Holt, 1965.

Kowdi, Jaisheela. *A comparative study of some teaching models for the cultivation of pupil's creativity.* Karnataka University, Dharwad, 1982.

Kumar, S., and Ravindranath, M.J. Development of creative thinking in primary school children. *The primary teacher,* NCERT, New Delhi, 1979, Vol. 4, No. 1, pp. 5-9.

Lehois, G. An analysis and synthesis of the concept of creativity. *Dissertation Abstracts,* 1963, Vol. 24, p. 1883.

Lowen feld, V. Currnet research on creativity. *Journal of the National Education Association,* 1958, Vol. 47, pp. 538-540.

Lowery, J. Developing creativity in gifted children. *Gifted Child Quarterly,* 1982, Vol. 2, pp. 133-39.

Lytton, H. and Cotton, A.C. Divergent thinking abilities in secondary schools. *British Journal of Educational Psychology.* 1969, Vol. 39, pp. 188-90.

Lytton, Hough: *Creativity and Education,* London, Routledge and Kegan Paul, 1971.

MacCallum, M.J. TM and Creativity in Orme-Johnson, D. and Farrow, J.T. *Scientific Research on the TM Programme (Vol. 1., Collected Papers).* NYC. Maharishi International University, 1975.

Mackinnon, D.W. The nature and nurture of Creative talent. *American Psychologists,* 1962, pp. 484-495.

Mackinnon, D.W. Identifying and developing creativity. *Journal of secondary Education,* 1963. Vol. 38, pp. 166-174.

Mackinnon, D.W. Instructional media in the nurturing of creativity. In C.W. Taylor and Frank E. Williams. *Instructional Media and Creativity.* New York, John Wiley and Sons, Inc., 1966, pp. 179-216.

Mackinnon, D.W. Education for Creativity: A modern myth? In P. Heist (Ed.) *Education for Creativity,* Berkeley: Centre for Research and Development in Higher Education, 1967, pp. 1-20.

Mackinnon, D.W. Research on Creativity. In M.K. Raina (Ed.) *Creativity Research: International Perspective.* National Institute of Education, NCERT., New Delhi, 1980, pp. 236-52.

Majumdar, S.K. A Systems approach to identification and nature of scientific creativity. *Journal of Indian Education,* 1977, Vol. 3, No.2, pp. 45-50.

Mansfield, R.E., Busse, T.V. and Krepelka, E.J. Effectiveness of Creativity Training Programme. *Review of Educational Research,* Fall, 1978, Vol. 48, No. 4, pp. 517-536.

Marksberry, M.L. *Foundation of Creativity,* N.Y. Harper, 1963.

Marlene, S.Z. Effect of an instructional use of programmed creativity training with gifted and regular students. *Journal of Educational Psychology,* 1979, Vol. 71, No. 3, pp. 303-309.

Mathur, R.N. Nurturing Creativity through instructional programmes. *Journal of Indian Education,* 1981, Vol. 7, No. 4, pp. 33-36.

Meadow. A., and Parnes, S.J. Evaluation of Training in Creative Problem Solving. *Journal of Applied Psychology,* 1959, Vol. 43, No. 4, pp. 189-194.

Meeker, M.N. *The Structure of Intellect: Its interpretation and uses.* Columbus, Ohio, Charles E. Merrill Publishing Co., 1969.

Meadow, A., Parnes, S.J., and Reese, H. Influence of Brainstorming instruction and problem sequence on creative problem solving test. *Journal of Applied Psychology,* 1959, Vol. 43, pp. 413-416.

Mehdi, Baquer. A survey of research in the area of creativity and implications for school practices. *Indian Educational Review,* 1966, Vol. 1, No.1., pp. 48-63.

Mehdi, Baquer. *Manual: Verbal test of creative thinking.* Published by Mrs. Qamar Fatima, Aligarh, 1973.

Mehdi, Baquer, *Manual: Non-verbal test of creative thinking.* Published by Mrs. Qamar Fatima, Aligarh, 1973.

Medhi, Baquer, Background paper. In Baquer Medhi (Editor). *Creativity in Teaching and Learning.* Report of the workshop conducted at the Regional College of Education, Mysore from 27th January to 1st February, 1975, RCE (NCERT) Mysore, 1977, pp. 1-4.

Mehdi, Baquer (Editor). *Creativity in Teaching and Learning.* Report of the workshop conducted at the Regional College of Education, Mysore from 27th Jan. to 1st February, 1975,

RCE (NCERT), Mysore, 1977, pp. 20-23.

Mehta, S.K. Can Creativity be fostered in students? *Educational Review.* 1983, Vol. 89, No. 8, pp. 135-38.

Mitchell, B.M. The classroom pursuit of creativity: one strategy that worked. *Journal of Research and Development.* Vol. 4, No. 3, pp. 57-62.

Miyan, Mohd. Study to exmaine the effectiveness of methods of teaching mathematics in developing creativity, *Unpublished Doctoral Dissertation.* Jamia Millia University, New Delhi, 1982.

Mooney, R. and Rezik, T. (Eds.). *Explorations in Creativity,* New York, Harper, 1967.

Myers, R.E. and Torrance, P.E. Can teachers encourage creative thinking? *Educatio ıal Leadership,* 1961, Vol. 19, pp. 156-159.

Myers, R.E. and Torrance, E.T. *Invitation to thinking and doing.* Boston: Genn and Co., 1964.

Myers, R.E. and Torrance, E.P. *Can you Imagine?* Boston: Ginn and Co., 1965(a).

Myers. R.E. and Torrance, E.P. *Invitations to speaking and writing creatively.* Ginn and Co., 1965 (b).

Myers, R.E., and Torrance, E.P. *For those who wonder.* Boston: Ginn and Co., 1966 (b).

Myers, R.E., and Torrance, E.P. *Plots, Puzzles, and Plays,* Boston: Ginn and Co., 1966 (b).

Myers, R.E. Torrance, E.P. *Strech. Minneapolis, Minnesota,* Perspective Publishing Company, 1968.

Nash, W.R. Effects of Warm-up activities on the creative thinking of disadvantaged first grade children. *Doctoral Dissertation,* University of Georgia, 1971.

NCERT, TM enhances creativity in students. *NCERT Newsletter,* New Delhi, July-Sept., 1980, Vol. Nos. 8-10.

Micholsen, P.J. An experimental investigation of the effects of training upon Creativity. *Doctoral Dissertation,* Houston, Texas: University of Houston, 1959.

Nirpharake, A.M. An experimental study of some methods of training in creativity (Unpublished Ph.D. Thesis, University of Poona, 1979). In M.B. Buch (Ed.) *Second Survey of Research in Education.*

Noller, R.B., and Parnes, S.J. Applied Creativity: The Creative Studies Project. Part III-The Curriculum. *Journal of Creative Behaviour,* 1972, Vol. 6, pp. 276-293.

Osborn, A.F. *Your Creative Power,* New York, Charles Scribners Sons, 1948.

Osborn, A.F. *Applied Imagination,* New York, Charles Scribners Sons, 1957.

Osborn, A.F. Developments in Creative Education. In S.J. Parnes and H.F. Harding. *A Source Book for Creative thinking,* New York: Charles Scribner's Sons, 1962.

Olton, Robert M. A Self instructional programme for developing productive thinking skills in V and VI grade children, *Journal of Creative Behaviour,* Fall, 1968, Vol. 2, No. 4.

Olton, R.M. and Crutchfield, R.S. (1969). Developing the skills of productive thinking. In G.A. Davis and J.A. Scott. Training Creative Thinking. New York, Holt, Rinehart and Winston, Inc., 1971, p. 238-260.

Parnes, S.J. (1963). Education and Creativity. In J.C. Gowan, G.D. Domos, and E.P. Torrance, *Creativity: Its Educational Implications,* New York. John Wiley and Sons, 1967, p. 33.

Parnes, S.J. Methods and Educational programmes for stimulating creativity: A representative list. *Journal of Creative Behaviour,* 1967. Vol. 2, No. 1.

Parnes, S.J. *Creative Behaviour workbook,* New York: Charles Scribner and Sons, 1967 (b).

Parnes, S.J. and Brunelle, E.A. The literature of creativity-Part I. *Journal of Creative Behaviour,* 1967, vol. 1, No. 1. pp. 52-109.

Parnes, S.J. The literature of creativity-Part II. *Journal of Creative Behaviour,* 1967, Vol. 2, pp. 191-239.

Parnes, S.J. *Creative Behaviour Guide Book,* N.Y. Charles: Scribners and Sons, 1967.

Parnes, S.J. Creativity: Developing human potential. *Journal of Creative Behaviour,* 1971, Vol. 5, No. 1, pp. 19-35.

Parnes, S.J. *Creativity Unlocking human potential.* Buffalo: D.O.K. 1972.

Parnes, S.J. Can creativity be increased? In G.A. Davis and J.A. Scott. *Training Creative Thinking,* New York, Holt, Rinehart and Winston, Inc., 1971, pp. 270-75.

Parnes, S.J. and Harding, H.F. (Eds.) *A Source Book for Creative thinking.* New York, Charles Scribner's Sons, 1962.

Parnes, S.J. and Meadow, A., Effects of brain-storming instruction on creative problem solving by trained and untrained subjects. *Journal of Educational Psychology,* 1959, Vol. 50, pp. 171-76.

Parnes, S.J. and Meadow, A. Evaluation of Persistence effects produced by a creative problem solving course. *Psychological Reports,* 1960, Vol. 7, pp. 357-361.

parnes, S.J. and Noller, R.B. Applied Creativity: The creative studies project, Part II-Results of the two year programme. *Journal of Creative Behaviour.* 1972, Vol. 6, pp. 164-186 (b).

Parnes, S.J. and Noller, R.B. Applied Creativity: The creative studies project, Part I-The development. *Journal of Creative Behaviour,* 1972, Vol. 6, pp. 11-20 (a).

Parnes, S.J. and Noller, N.B. Applied Creativity: The creative studies project Part IV, Personality findings and conclusions.

*Journal of Creative Behaviour,* 1973, Vol. 7, pp. 15-36.

Passi, B.K. Definition of creativity - A review study. *Creativity Newsletter,* 1973, Vol. 2, No. 2, pp. 5-10.

Passi, B.K., Sansanwal, D.N., and Jarial, G.S. Creativity and Education. *National Psychological Corporation,* Agra, 1982.

Passi, B.K. and Jarial, G.S. Research on creativity training in India: A review. In Govind Tewari and Roma Pal (Eds.) *Status of Indian Researches in Creativity,* Agra Psychological Research Cell, Agra, 1983, pp. 45-54.

Patrick, C. *What is Creative Thinking?* New York, Philosophical Library, Inc., 1956.

Penick, J.E. The effects of two patterns of teaching on aspects of verbal and figural creativity in fifth grade science students. *Dissertation Abstracts,* 1973, Vol. 24, p. 4029-A.

Pillay, G.S. Effects of Patterns of Teaching upon creative thinking among adolescents (Unpublished Doctoral Dissertation, M.S. University, Baroda, 1978). In M.B. Buch (Ed.) *Second Survey of Research in Education.*

Pillay, G.S. Effects of Creative Teaching Method upon eighth graders. *Journal of Indian Education,* 1979, Vol. 5, No. 4, pp. 12-16.

Possien (1964). A comparison of the effects of three teaching methodologies on the development of the problem solving skills of sixth grade children. *Dissertation Abstracts,* 1965, Vol. 25, No. 7, p. 4003.

Prasad, V. Promotion of Creativity and Achievement by discovery method. *Indian Education Review,* 1979, Vol. 14, No. 4, pp. 86-94.

Prince, G.M. *The Practice of Creativity,* N.Y. Harper and Row, 1972.

Raina, M.K. Developing Creativity in Children. *Education Qrtly.*, 1967, Vol. 19, No. 2, pp. 55-56.

Raina, M.K. and Chaturvedi, S. Effects of training in creative problem solving on fluency of thinking. *Indian Journal of Applied Psychology,* 1970, Vol. 7, pp. 71-74.

Raina, M.K. Research developments in creativity in India. *Journal of Research and Development in Education,* 1971 (a), Vol. 3, pp. 118-128.

Raina, M.K. (Editor). *Creativity Research: International Perspective,* New Delhi, NCERT, 1980.

Raina, M.K. Research on Creativity in India. In M.K. Raina (Ed.) *Creativity Research: International Perspective,* New Delhi, NCERT, 1980.

Ramey, C.T. and Piper, V. Creativity in open and Traditional Class rooms. *Child Development,* 1974, Vol. 45, No. 2, pp. 557-560.

Razik, T.M. An investigation of Creative thinking among college students. *Dissertation Abstracts,* 1964, Vol. 24, No. 7, p. 2775-A.

Reese, H.W. Parnes, S.J., Treffinger, D.J. and Kaltsounis, G. Effects of a creative studies programme on structure of Intellect factors. *Journal of Educational Psychology,* 1976, Vol. 68, pp. 401-410.

Renjulli, J.S. *New Directions in Creativity,* Harper and Row, 1973.

Rhodes, M. An analysis of creativity. *Phi-Delta Kappan,* 1961, Vol. 42, pp. 305-10.

Ridley, D.R., and Birney, R.C. Effects of training procedures on creativity test scores. *Journal of Educational Psychology,* 1967, Vol. 58, pp. 158-64.

Ripple, R.E. and Dacey, J. The facilitation of problem solving and verbal creativity by exposure to programmed instruction. *Psychology in the schools,* 1967, Vol. 4, pp. 240-245.

Rogers, C.R. Towards a theory of creativty. In H.H. Anderson

(Ed.) *Creativity and its Cultivation,* N.Y. Harper, 1959.

Rouse, Laura Hall, and Lin, Hsin-Tin. A meta-analysis of long term creativity training programme. *Journal of Creative Behaviour,* 1984, Vol. 18, No. 1, pp. 11-22.

Roweton, W.E. *Creativity: A review of theory and research.* The Creative Education Foundation, Occasional paper No. 7, 1973, pp. 1-25.

Rush, R.R. (*et al.*). Fostering Creativity in the Sixth grade and its effect on achievement. *Journal of Experimental Education,* 1967, Vol. 36, No. 1, pp. 80-86.

Sandhu, T.S. Does Creativity influence academic achievement, *Journal of Indian Education,* 1978, Vol. 4, No. 3, pp. 49-55.

Sansanwal, D.N., Stahe, S, and Jarial, G.S. Faciliation of creative thinking abilities through transcendental meditation. *Journal of Indian Education,* 1980, Vol. 6, No. 3, pp. 9-13.

Schecter, H. The TM programme in the class room. In D. Orme-Johnson and J. T. Farrow. *Scientific Research on the TM Programme* (Vol. 1, Collected papers) NYC. Maharishi International University, 1975.

Schuler, G. *The effectiveness of the Productive thinking programme,* Ithaca, N.Y.: Ithaca College, 1974.

Stein, M.I. A transactional approach to creativity. In C.W. Taylor, *Report of the 1955 University of Utah Research Conference on the Identification of Creative Scientific Talent,* 1956, pp. 171-174.

Stein, Morris I. *Stimulating Creativity,* Vol. 1 & 2, Academic Press, Inc., New York, 1974.

Steinmetz, C.S. (1965). Creativity training: A testing programme that became a sales training programme. In G.A. Davis and J.A. Scott (Eds). *Training Creative Thinking,* New York, Holt, Rinehart and Winston, Inc., 1971.

Shackel, D.S. and Lawrence, P.J. Improving Creativity Through programmed instruction. *New Zealand Journal of Educational Studies,* 1969, Vol. 4, pp. 41-56.

Sharma, A.P. *Anatomy of Creativity.* Psycholingua Publication, Raipur, 1972.

Sharma, K.N. *Dynamics of Creativity,* National Psychological Corporation, Agra, 1979.

Sharma, K.K., and Gupta, P.K. Curriculum and Talent development. *In the Report of the Workshop Organized by the Curriculum Group,* NCERT, New Delhi, 1982.

Shively, J.E. Evaluation of the effects of creativity training programme in the elementary school. *Dissertation Abstracts,* 1971, Vol. 31, No. 10, p. 5215-A.

Shively, J.E., Feldhusen, J.F., and Treffinger, D.J. Developing Creativity and Related attitudes. *Journal of Experimental Education,* 1972, Vol. 41, No. 2, pp. 63-69.

Shrikhande, M.S. Teaching for critical and creative thinking: A study. *Indian Educational Review,* 1983, Vol. 17, No. 2, pp. 91-93.

Sinha, A.K.P. Fostering Creative habits in educational system. *Indian Journal of Psychometry and Education,* 1971, Vol. 2, No. 1 & 2.

Singh, Didar. *Scientific Creativity and Personality.* National Psychological Corporation, Agra, 1981.

Singh, K. Problems in measurement of creative thinking. *ISPT Journal of Research in Educational and Psychological Measurement,* 1982, Vol. 4, No. 2, pp. 22-25.

Singh, R.P. Education for Creativity. *Indian Psychological Review,* 1977, Vol. 14, No. 2, pp. 67-68.

Smith, I. and Leon, I.Q. Creativity and the taxonomy of educational objectives: Cognitive domain. *Journal of Experimental Education,* 1970, Vol. 38, No. 4, p. 5860.

Sommers, W.S. The influence of selected teaching methods on the development of creative thinking. *Unpublished Doctoral Dissertation.* University of Minnesota, 1961, Dissertation Abstract, 1962, Vol. 22, No. 11, p. 3954-A.

Speedie, S.M., Treffinger, D.J. Feldhusen, J.F. Evaluation of components of the Purdue Creative thinking programme: A longitudinal study. *Psychological Reports,* 1971, Vol. 29, pp. 395-398.

Springer, Thomas, A. An experimental study of the group counselling upon the creative thinking of selected senior, high school students. *Dissertation Abstract,* 1970, Vol. 31, No. 1.

Suchman, J.R. Inquiry Training in the elementary schools. *Science Teacher,* 1960, Vol. 27, No. 42-43, pp. 45-47.

Suchman, J.R. Inquiry Training: Building Skills for autonomous discovery. Merrill-Palmer *Quarterly Behaviour Development,* 1961, Vol. 7, pp. 147-169.

Tadlock, Sharon Elaine. The effect of a Basis Movement education programme on the creative thinking skills and self-concept of Gifted students. *Dissertation Abstract,* 1980, Vol. 41, No. 8, p. 3407-A.

Taylor, C.W. *Identification of Creative Scientific Talent. American Psychologist,* 1959, Vol. 14, pp. 100-102.

Taylor, C.W. Effects of instructional media on creativity: a look at possible positive and negative effects. *Educational Leadership,* 1962(b), Vol. 19, No. 7, pp. 453-58.

Taylor, C.W. Some educational implications of creativity research findings. *School Science and Mathematics,* (1962(c), Vol. 62, No. 8, pp. 593-606.

Taylor, C.W. Who are exceptionally creative? *Exceptional Child,* 1962 (d), Vol. 28, No. 8, pp. 421-431.

Taylor, C.W. *Are we utilizing our creative potential? Nursing*

*Outlook.* 1963, Vol. II, No. 2, pp. 105-107.

Taylor, C.W. (Ed.) *Creativity: Progress and Potential,* New York, McGraw Hill, 1964.

Taylor, C.W. (Ed.) *Widening Horizons in Creativity,* New York, Wiley, 1964.

Taylor, C.W. and Williams, F.E. (Eds.) *Instructional Media and Creativity,* New York, Wiley, 1966.

Taylor, C.W. (Ed.) Climate for Creativity, *Report of the Seventh National Research Conference on Creativity,* New York, John Wiley and Sons, Inc., 1972.

Taylor, I. and Gatzels, J.W. *Perspectives in Creativity.* Chicago: Aldine, 1975.

Teeling, T. (1979). The effect of the multi-talent approach to teaching on the creative thinking performance of elementary students. *Dissertation Abstracts,* 1980, Vol. 40, p. 3751-A.

Tewari, G. and Pal. P. *Status of Indian Researches in Creativity.* Agra Psychological Research Cell, Agra, 1983.

Torrance, E.P. (Editor). *Talent and Education.* Minneapolis, Minnesota, University of Minnesota Press, 1960.

Torrance, E.P. Must Creative development be left to chance. *Gifted Child Quarterly,* 1962, Vol. 6, pp. 41-44.

Torrance, E.P. Giving Children a Chance to Learn and Think Creatively. In E.P. Torrance (Ed.) *Education and Creative Potential,* The University of Minnesota Press, Minneapolis, 1963, pp. 56-58.

Torrance, E.P. Developing Creative Thinking through School Experiences. In S.J. Parnes, and H.E. Hardings (Eds.) *A Source Book of Creative Thinking,* New York, Charles: Scribner and Sons, 1962, pp. 31-47.

Tottance, E.P. *Guiding Creative Talent.* Englewood Cliffs, N.J. Prentice-Hall, Inc., 1962.

Torrance, E.P. Ten Ways of Helping Young Children Gifted

in Creative Writing and Speech. *Gifted Child Quarterly,* 1962, Vol. 6, pp. 121-127.

Torrance, E.P. Explorations in Creative Thinking in the early School Years. In C.W. Tylor and F. Barron (Eds.) *Scientific Creativity: Its Recognition and Development.* New York, Wiley, 1963, pp. 173-183.

Torrance, E.P. *Creativity and Intelligence,* Minnesota Bureau of Educational Research, Spring, 1963 (b).

Torrance, E.P. *Education and the Creative Potential.* Minneapolis, University of Minnestota Press, 1963.

Torrance, E.P. Creativity in the Class room: Respecting Children's questions and ideas. *The Instructor,* September, 1964, Vol. 37, p. 129.

Torrance, E.P. Creative Teaching makes a difference. *Bureau of Educational Research,* University of Minnesota, 1964.

Torrance, E.P., and R. Gupta, Development and Evaluation of Recorded Programmed experiences in Creative Thinking in the fourth grade. Minneapolis: *Bureau of Educational Research.* University of Minnesota, 1964.

Torrance, E.P. *Gifted Children in the Class room,* New York, Macmillan, 1965.

Torrance, E.P. and Hansen, E. The Question asking behaviour of highly creative and less creative basic teachers identified by a paper-pencil test. *Psychological Reports,* 1965, Vol. 17, No. 5, pp. 815-818.

Torrance, E.P. *Rewarding Creative Behaviour.* Englewood Cliffs, N.J. Prentlice-Hall, Inc., 1965.

Torrance, E.P. Implications of creativity research findings for instructional media. In C.W. Taylor and F.E. William (Eds.) *Instructional Media and Creativity,* New York, Willey, 1966.

Torrnace, E.P. The Minnesota Studies of Creative Behaviour: National and International extension. *Journal of Creative Be-*

*haviour,* 1967, Vol. 1, No. 2, pp. 137-154.

Torrance, E.P. *Encouraging Creativity in the Class room.* Dubesque, Iowa : WmC. Brown Company Publishers, 1970.

Torrance, E.P. Causes for concern. In P.E. Verson (Ed.) *Creativity.* Penguin Books Ltd., England, 1970, pp. 355-370.

Torrance, E.P. and Khatena, J. What kind of Person are you? : A brief screening device for identifying creatively gifted a dolescents and adults. *Gifted Child Quarterly,* 1970, Vol. 14, No. 2, pp. 71-75.

Torrance, E.P. and Myers, R.E. *Creative Learning and Teaching,* New York: Dodd, Mead, 1970.

Torrnace, E.P. Nature of Creative Talents. In G.A. Davis and J.A. Scott (Eds.) *Training Creative Thinking,* New York, Holt, Rinehart and Winston, Inc., 1971.

Torrance, E.P. Can we teach children to think creatively? *Journal of Creative Behaviour,* 1972, Vol. 6, pp. 236-262 (b).

Torrance, E.P., Khatena, J., and Cunnington, B.F. *Thinking Creatively with Sounds and Words, Lexington,* Mass : Personnel Press, 1973.

Torrance, E.P., and Torrance, J.P. Is Creativity Teachable? Bloomington, Ind: *Phi Delta Kappa,* Educational Foundation, 1973.

Torrance, E.P. Status of Creativity Research: Early 1974 (Editorial). *The Eduational Trends,* 1973, Vol. 8, No. 1-4.

Torrance, E.P. (1975). After twenty-five years: what do we know about creativity. In M.K. Raina (Ed.) *Creativity Research: International perspective,* National Institute of Education, NCERT, 1980, pp. 275-281.

Toynbee, A. Is America neglecting her creative minority? In C.W. Taylor (Ed.) *Widening Horizons in Creativity,* New York, John Wiley and Sons, Inc., 1964.

Traft, Ronald and Gilcharist, Margaret B. Creative attitudes and creative productivity: A comparison of two aspects of creativity among students. *Journal of Educational Psychology,* 1970, Vol. 61, No. 2, pp. 136-143.

Treffinger, D.J. The effects of programmed instruction in productive thinking on verbal creativity and problem solving among pupils in grade four, five, six and seven. *Unpublished Doctoral Dissertation,* Ithaca: Cornell University, 1969.

Treffinger, D.J. *Improving children's Creative Problem solving abilities: Effects of distribution of training, teacher involvement and teacher's divergent thinking ability on instruction.* (Final Report) Office of Education, Indian, Purdue University, 1971.

Treffinger, D.J. (Editor) *Readings on Creativity in Education.* Prentice Hall, New York, 1972.

Treffinger, D.J. Teaching for self-directed learning: A priority for the gifted and talented. *Gifted Child Quarterly,* 1975, Vol. 29, pp. 46-59.

Treffinger, D.J. Methods, techniques and educational Programmes for stimulating creativity (1975 revision). In S.J. Parnes, R.B. Noller, and A.M. Binodi (Eds.) *Guide to Creative Action,* New York, Charles, Scribner and Sons, 1977.

Treffinger, D.J. *Encouraging Creative Learning for the Gifted and Talented: A Hand Book of Methods and Techniques,* LTI Publications, Ventura, California, 1978.

Treffinger, D.A., and Huber, J.R. Designing instruction in Creative Problem solving: Preliminary Objectives and Learning Hierarchies. *Journal of Creative Behaviour,* 1975, Vol. 9, pp. 260-66.

Treffinger, D.J., and Ripple, R.E. Developing Creative Problem solving abilities and related attitudes through programmed instruction. *Journal of Creative Behaviour.* 1969, Vol. 3, No. 2, pp. 105-110.

Treffinger, D.A., and Ripple, R.E. The Effect of Programmed instruction of Creative Problem solving and attitude. *Irish Journal of Education,* 1970, Vol. 4, pp. 47-59.

Treffinger, D.J., Renjulli, J.S. and Feldhusen, J.F. Problems in the assessment creative thinking. *Journal of Creative Behaviour,* 1971, Vol. 5, pp. 104-112.

Treffinger, D.J. Speedie, S.M. and Bruner, W.D. Improving children's Creative Problem solving ability. The Purdue Creativity Project. *Journal of Creative Behaviour,* 1974, Vol. 8, No. 1, pp. 20-30.

Tripathi, S.N. *Creativity and Education.* Regional College of Education, Bhopal, NCERT, New Delhi, 1969.

Trowbridge, N. Research on Creativity. In A.S. Patel and G.B. Shah (Eds.) *Educational of the Backwards and the Gifted Children,* CASE, Baroda, 1966.

Turner, W.M., and Rains, J.D. Differential effective of Brainstorming instruction upon high and low creative subject. *Psychological Reports,* 1965, Vol. 17, pp. 753-754.

Tweet, Claudia Clague. The effects of the implementation of creativity training in the elementary school social studies curriculum. *Journal of Creative Behaviour,* 1981, Vol. 15, No. 1, pp. 70-71.

Vernon, P.E. Creativity and Intelligence. *Educational Research,* 1964, Vol. 6, No. 3, pp. 163-96.

Vernon, P.E. (Ed. *Creativity.* Penguin Books Ltd., Harmondsworth, Middesex, England, 1970.

Vervalin, C.H. Just what is creativity? In G.A. Davis and J.A. Scott (Eds.) *Training Creative Thinking,* New York, Holt, Rinehart and Winston, 1971.

Wardrop, J.L., Olton, R.M., Goodwin, W.L., Covington, M.V., Klausmeier, H.J., Crutchfield, R.S. and Ronda, T. The development of productive thinking skills in fifth grade children. *Journal of Experimental Education,* 1969, Vol. 37, pp. 67-77.

Walker, W.J., Creativity and high school climate. In J.C. Gowan, G.D. Demos, and E.P. Torrance, *Creativity: Its Educational Implications,* N.Y. Wiley, 1967.

Warrne, T.F. and Davis, G.A. Techniques for creative thinking: Empirical comparison of three methods. *Psychological Reports,* 1960, Vol. 25, No.1, pp. 207-214.

Warren, T.F. Creative thinking techniques: Four methods of stimulating original ideas in six grade students. *Dissertation Abstracts,* 1971, Vol. 31, No. 11, p. 5863-A.

William, F.F. *Foundations of Creative Problem Solving.* Ann Arbor,. Michigan, Edward Bros, Inc, 1960.

William, F.E. Fostering class room creativity. *California Teachers Association Journal.* Feb., 1962, pp. 19-20.

Williams, F.E. *A total Creativity Training Programme for Individualizing and Humanizing the Learning Process.* Englewood Cliffs N.J.P. Educational Technology, Publications, 1972.

Wilt, M.E. *Creativity in the elementary school,* N.Y. Appleton Century Crofts, Inc., 1959.

Winer, B.J. *Statistical Principles in Experimental Design,* New York: McGraw-Hill, 1962.

Witty, P.C., James, B., and Strang, R. *Creativity of Gifted and Talented Children.* Columbia University, Bureau of Publications, Teacher's College, 1959, p. 51.

Wodtke, K.H. and Wallen, N.E. Teacher Class room Control, Pupil Creativity and Pupil class room behavicur. *Journal of Experimental Education,* 1965, Vol. 34, No.1, pp. 59-65.

Wood, Dennis. The Effects of Different Teaching Styles on Creativity. *Journal of Creative Behaviour.* 1976, Vol. 10, No. 3, p. 220.

Yamamoto, K. Do creativity tests really measure creativity? *Theory into practice,* 1966, Vol. 5, pp. 194-197.

Yamamoto, K. Does Teacher Creativity make a difference in pupil learning? *Elementary School Journal.* 1967, Vol. 5, pp. 265-270.

Zirbez, L. *Spurs of Creative Teaching,* N.Y. G.P. Putnam and Sons, 1959.